蔡志忠漫画中英文版

庄子说 ①

ZHUANG ZI SPEAKS Ⅰ

自·然·的·箫·声

The Music of Nature

蔡志忠/著　BRIAN BRUYA(美)/译

现代出版社

Contents

Zhuangzi Speaks I
The Music of Nature

亢桑子之属，皆空语无事实，然善属书离辞，指事情类，用剽剥儒墨，虽当世宿学不能自解免也。其言洸洋自恣以适己，故自王公大人不能器之。

庄子者，蒙人也，名周。周尝为蒙漆园吏，与梁惠王、齐宣王同时。其学无所不窥，然其要本归于老子之言。故其著书十余万言，大抵率寓言也。作渔父、盗跖、胠箧，以诋訿孔子之徒，以明老子之术。畏累虚、

《汉·司马迁◎史记》

自然的箫声——庄子说Ⅰ

Zhuangzi

自然的箫吉——主子兑Ⅰ

亢桑子之属，皆空语无事实，然善属书离辞，指事情类，用剽剥儒墨，虽当世适己，故自王公大人不能器之。之言。故其著书十余万言，大抵率寓言也。作渔父、盗跖、胠箧，以诋讹孔子之徒，以明老子之术。畏累虚、庄子者，蒙人也，名周。周尝为蒙漆园吏，与梁惠王、齐宣王同时。其学无所不窥，然其要本归于老子

《汉·司马迁◎史记》

2

The name of our hero is Zhuang Zhou, and like all Chinese names, the surname comes first, followed by the given name. To show respect for his vast wisdom, we add the word zi to his surname, just like Kongzi (Confucius), Mengzi (Mencius), and Laozi. Zhuangzi lived during the fourth century B.C., a time known as the Warring States period in China. This was a period of disunity in which rival nations battled constantly for more land and greater power. As a result, it was also a time or widespread death and destruction. Zhuangzi saw this and was deeply saddened by it.

1

2

As a way out, Zhuangzi shifted his line of sight from the earthly world to the limitlessness of time and space.

自然的箫吉——庄子说Ⅰ

庄子者，姓庄，名周，（太史公云：字子休。）梁国蒙县人也。六国时，为漆园吏，与魏惠王、齐宣王、楚威王同时，（李颐云：与齐愍王同时。）齐楚尝聘以为相，不应。时人皆尚游说，庄子独高尚其事，优游自得，依老氏之旨，著书十余万言，以逍遥自然无为齐物而已；大抵皆寓言，归之于理，不可案文责也。

《唐·陆德明○庄子序》

7
Don't draw life from death.
Only in this way can you attain limitless freedom.

8
The philosophy of Zhuangzi is a philosophy of freedom. It is a philosophy which takes life and hurls it into the limitlessness of time and space in order to be experienced to the fullest.

9
To Zhuangzi, the world was chained by a "lifeless order", so what he pursued instead was a "lively disorder".

自然的箫声——庄子说[

《唐·成玄英◎庄子序》

夫庄子者，所以申道德之深根，述重玄之妙旨，畅无为之恬淡，明独化之窅冥，钳揵九流，括囊百氏，谅区中之至教，实象外之微言者也。

苍生之业薄，伤道德之陵夷，乃慷慨发愤，爰著斯论。其言大而博，其旨深而远，非下士之所闻，岂浅识之能究！

其人姓庄，名周，字子休，生宋国睢阳蒙县，师长桑公子，受号南华仙人。当战国之初，降周之末，叹

人匹之，不亦悲乎！

灵者，以五百岁为春，五百岁为秋；上古有大椿者，以八千岁为春，八千岁为秋。而彭祖乃今以久特闻，众

小知不及大知，小年不及大年。奚以知其然也？朝菌不知晦朔，蟪蛄不知春秋，此小年也。楚之南有冥

《庄子◎逍遥游第一》

The Winter Cicada and the Wonder Tortoise

People say that once there was a man named Peng Zu, who at 800 years old had lived the longest life ever.

Wow, he is old!

You can say that again!

1

In contrast, there is a small bug called the Zhaojun that is born in the morning and is dead by nightfall.

2

It doesn't even know what a month is.

3

There is also an insect called the winter cicada, which is born in the Spring and dies in the Summer.

4

It doesn't even know what the four seasons are.

5

However, in the southern part of Chu, there lived the giant wonder tortoise, to whom five hundred years was a mere Spring.

6

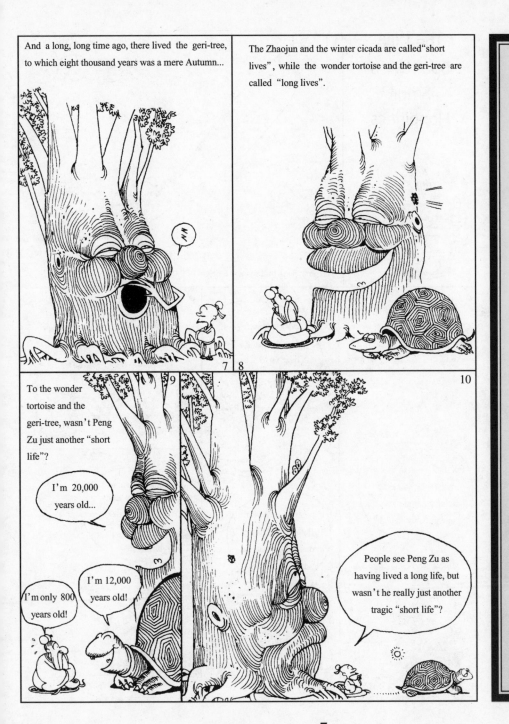

人匹之，不亦悲乎！

灵者，以五百岁为春，五百岁为秋；上古有大椿者，以八千岁为春，八千岁为秋。而彭祖乃今以久特闻，众

小知不及大知，小年不及大年。奚以知其然也？朝菌不知晦朔，蟪蛄不知春秋，此小年也。楚之南有冥

自然的箫声——庄子说I

《庄子◎逍遥游第一》

也。而彼且奚适也？」此小大之辩也。

南，且适南冥也。斥鴳笑之曰：「彼且奚适也？我腾跃而上，不过数仞而下，翱翔蓬蒿之间，此亦飞之至

有鸟焉，其名为鹏，背若太山，翼若垂天之云，搏扶摇羊角而上者九万里，绝云气，负青天，然后图

汤之问棘也是已。穷发之北有冥海者，天池也。有鱼焉，其广数千里，未有知其修者，其名为鲲。

《庄子◎逍遥游第一》

The Little Sparrow's Small Happiness

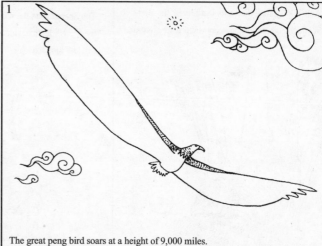

Hui Shi's Giant Gourd

自然的箫声——庄子说Ⅰ

惠子谓庄子曰：「魏王贻我大瓠之种，我树之成而实五石，以盛水浆，其坚不能自举也；剖之以为瓢，则瓠落无所容。非不呺然大也，吾为其无用而掊之。」

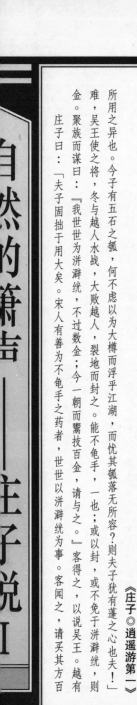

自然的箫声——庄子说 I

庄子曰：「夫子固拙于用大矣。宋人有善为不龟手之药者，世世以洴澼絖为事。客闻之，请买其方百金。聚族而谋曰：『我世世为洴澼絖，不过数金；今一朝而鬻技百金，请与之。』客得之，以说吴王。越有难，吴王使之将，冬与越人水战，大败越人，裂地而封之。能不龟手，一也；或以封，或不免于洴澼絖，则所用之异也。今子有五石之瓠，何不虑以为大樽而浮乎江湖，而忧其瓠落无所容？则夫子犹有蓬之心也夫！」

《庄子◎逍遥游第一》

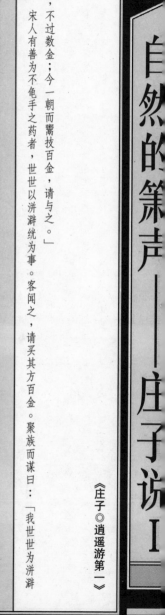

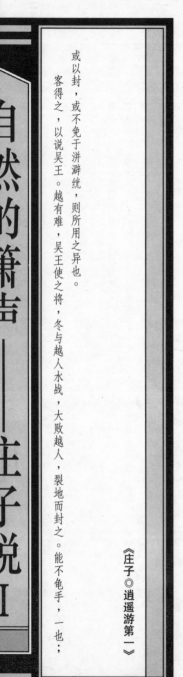

或以封，或不免于洴澼絖，则所用之异也。

客得之，以说吴王。越有难，吴王使之将，冬与越人水战，大败越人，裂地而封之。能不龟手，一也；

《庄子○逍遥游第一》

At that time, the states of Wu and Yue were bitter enemies.

Wu   Yue

After getting the secret formula for this medicine, the king of Wu launched a winter offensive on water.

The Wu army relied on this medicine not to get frostbite, but the Yue soldiers were unprotected. As a result, the Yue army was terribly defeated.

After the defeat of the Yue kingdom, the traveler who presented the secret formula to the king of Wu was conferred with a large estate and lived the life of a nobleman thereafter.

Although it was the same formula, some people didn't know how to use it, so they spent their lives bleaching cloth. But when a flexible person who could think of new ideas came along, he ended up living a life of luxury.

12

The Useless Shu Tree

1. Huizi once said to Zhuangzi: I have this giant tree called a *shu* tree. Its trunk is all lumps and bumps and winds this way and that.

2. Its branches are all gnarled and twisted. A carpenter's plumb line could never be used on it.

3. It grows right beside the road, and no carpenter has ever paid any attention to it.

4. The words you have been speaking lately are just like this tree, big and useless. Who's going to listen to you?

自然的箫声——庄子说 I

者不顾。今子之言，大而无用，众所同去也。」

惠子谓庄子曰：「吾有大树，人谓之樗。其大本拥肿而不中绳墨，其小枝卷曲而不中规矩，立之涂，匠

13

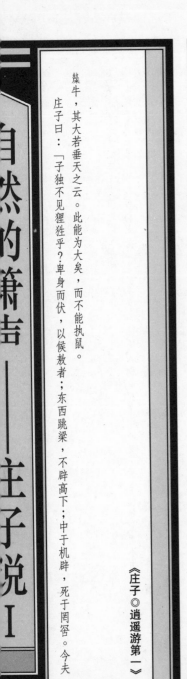

《庄子◎逍遥游第一》

自然的箫声——主子说 I

犛牛，其大若垂天之云。此能为大矣，而不能执鼠。

庄子曰：「子独不见狸狌乎？卑身而伏，以候敖者；东西跳梁，不辟高下；中于机辟，死于罔罟。今夫

5 Have you ever seen a fox or a wildcat? In order to catch their prey, they are always jumping over things and running all over the place; and although they are very agile,

6 Eventually, they will fall into a trap and die.

As for the yak, although it is big, like a giant cloud hanging in the sky,

It couldn't catch a mouse if it wanted to.

斤斧，物无害者，无所可用，安所困苦哉！」

今子有大树，患其无用，何不树之于无何有之乡。广莫之野，彷徨乎无为其侧，逍遥乎寝卧其下。不夭

15

自然的箫吉——主子说 I

宋人资章甫而适诸越，越人断发文身，无所用之。尧治天下之民，平海内之政，往见四子藐姑射之山，汾水之阳，窅然丧其天下焉。

《庄子◎逍遥游第一》

The Tattooed Yue People

One day, a man from Song went to Yue to sell hats and shirts, thinking he could make lots of money.

Get yer shirts! Beeyooteeful hats and shirts for sale!

What he didn't know was that the Yue people had a custom of cutting their hair short and not wearing shirts because they tattooed their bodies.

Useless stuff.

Useful and useless, achievement and failure, are all relative, and none are necessarily consistent over time. The achievement and failure of the ancient kings Yao and Shun are like the usefulness and uselessness of the Song man's garments, nothing is for sure.

Useful | Useless

自然的箫声——庄子说 I

「天籟夫！」

子綦曰：「偃，不亦善乎，而問之也，今者吾喪我，汝知之乎？女聞人籟而未聞地籟，女聞地籟而未聞天籟而心固可使如死灰乎？今之隱机者，非昔之隱机者也。」

南郭子綦隱机而坐，仰天而噓？答焉似喪其耦。顏成子游立侍乎前，曰：「何居乎？形固可使如槁木，

17

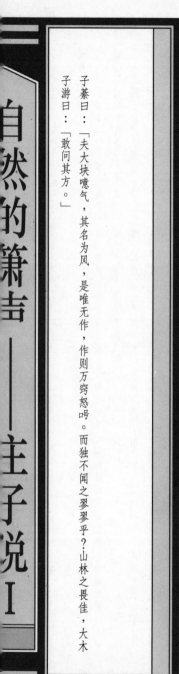

子綦曰：「夫大块噫气，其名为风，是唯无作，作则万窍怒呺。而独不闻之翏翏乎？山林之畏佳，大木

子游曰：「敢问其方。」

自然的箫声——主子说I

果且有成与亏乎哉？果且无成与亏乎哉？有成与亏，故昭氏之鼓琴也；无成与亏，故昭氏之不鼓琴也。是非之彰也，道之所以亏也。道之所以亏，爱之所以成。

未始有封也。其次以为有封焉，而未始有是非也。是非之彰也，道之所以亏也。

古之人，其知有所至矣。恶乎至？有以为未始有物者，至矣，尽矣，不可以加矣。其次以为有物矣，而

《庄子◎齐物论第二》

Zhao Wen Quits the Zither

1 Once there was a famous Zither player named Zhao Wen, who could play the Zither like no one else.

2 But one day, Zhao Wen suddenly stopped playing the zither altogether.

3 He finally realized that in playing one sound, it would be to the neglect of all the other sounds...

4 It was only when he wasn't playing, that he could hear everything in complete harmony.

The principles of music and wood carving are alike — when a wood carving is finished, it has been created at the expense of all the wood that has been carved away. Only the music of nature is complete and undiminished.

自然的箫声——主子兑I

之端，是非之涂，樊然殽乱，吾恶能知其辩！

嫱丽姬，人之所美也；鱼见之深入，鸟见之高飞，麋鹿见之决骤。四者孰知天下之正色哉？自我观之，仁义

民食刍豢，麋鹿食荐，蝍蛆甘带，鸱鸦嗜鼠，四者孰知正味？猿猵狙以为雌，麋与鹿交，鳅与鱼游。毛

且吾尝问乎女：民湿寝则腰疾偏死，鳅然乎哉？木处则惴栗恂惧，猿猴然乎哉？三者孰知正处？

虽然，尝试言之。庸讵知吾所谓知之非不知邪？庸讵知吾所谓不知之非知邪？

曰：「吾恶乎知之！」

《庄子◎齐物论第二》

8 People, mudfish, and monkeys all live in different places. Where's the standard?

9 Right! Everyone's standard is different...

Exactly!

10
People eat meat

Deer eat grass.

Centipedes eat snakes,

Crows eat mice,

11 These four kinds of animals are all different. Who's to say which of their diets is right?

Standards are different for all things, so the standard set by man is by no means the only "certain" standard. If you mistake what is relative for something certain, you have strayed far from the ultimate Dao.

Is Xi Shi Really Beautiful?

1. If from the beginning we had called the sky "horse,"

horse
horse

2. And called the ground "point",

point
point

3. Then the sky would be "horse" and the ground would be "point".

horse
point

4. When people think that something is wrong, they say "wrong". And when they think that something is right, they say "right". But what are the standards of "right" and "wrong"?

In creating knowledge from subjectivity, people trap themselves in their own limited world.

5. People think that Xi Shi is beautiful, but what would a fish think? If a fish saw Xi Shi, it might very well swim away in disgust.

Gorgeous!

Gross!

之，仁义之端，是非之涂，樊然殽乱，吾恶能知其辩！

毛嫱丽姬，人之所美也；鱼见之深入，鸟见之高飞，麋鹿见之决骤。四者孰知天下之正色哉？自我观

且吾尝试问乎女：民湿寝则腰疾偏死，鳅然乎哉？木处则惴栗恂惧，猿猴然乎哉？三者孰知正处？民食

之，麋鹿食荐，蝍且甘带，鸱鸦嗜鼠，四者孰知正味？猿猵狙以为雌，麋与鹿交，鳅与鱼游。

《庄子◎齐物论第二》

Li Ji's Tears

On Li Ji's wedding day, she was to be married to Prince Jin Xian. She was so sad that she drenched her wedding dress in tears.

I'm not marrying him! I won't do it!

But after she was married, she found herself sleeping on a long, soft bed and eating food from the four corners of the earth. Who would believe that on her wedding day, she cried her eyes out?

Everyone is afraid of dying, but maybe death will be so great that we'll end up regretting having ever lived.

Zhang Wuzi's Dream

1

A person having a dream is never aware of it, and in his dream he might even do things like predict his own fate. Only after he wakes up does he realize that he was dreaming.

Zhang Wuzi said to Ju Que:

2

Only the truly enlightened person realizes that life is just one big dream. And then there are those fools who think that they are the enlightened ones.

3

You and I are both dreaming. When I say you are dreaming, that is mere dream talk.

You're dreaming!

Only those who have great doubts can be truly enlightened. But a fool always believes that he is enlightened, and that is why in the end, he is a fool.

也；予谓女梦，亦梦也。是其言也，其名为吊诡。万世之后而一遇大圣，知其解者，是旦暮遇之也。

且有大觉而后知此其大梦也，而愚者自以为觉，窃窃然知之。君乎，牧乎，固哉！丘也与女，皆梦梦饮酒者，旦而哭泣；梦哭泣者，旦而田猎。方其梦也，不知其梦也。梦之中又占其梦焉，觉而后知其

《庄子◎齐物论第二》

Dialogue With a Shadow

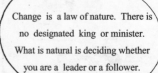

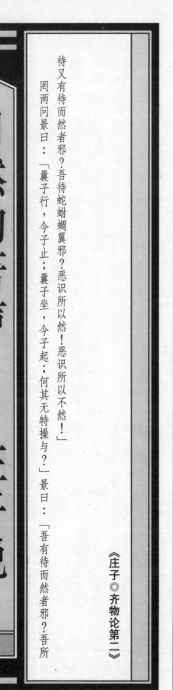

《庄子◎齐物论第二》

自然的箴言——庄子说

罔两问景曰：「曩子行，今子止；曩子坐，今子起；何其无特操与？」景曰：「吾有待而然者邪？吾所待又有待而然者邪？吾待蛇蚹蜩翼邪？恶识所以然！恶识所以不然！」

The Dream of the Butterfly

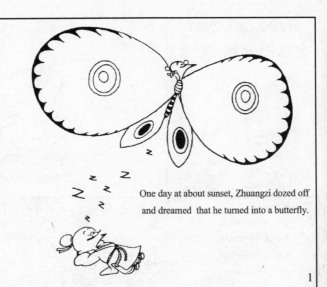

One day at about sunset, Zhuangzi dozed off and dreamed that he turned into a butterfly.

1

2 He flapped his wings, and , sure enough, he was a butterfly, what a joyful feeling. As he fluttered about, he completely forgot that he was Zhuangzi.

Soon, though, he realized that that proud butterfly was in fact Zhuangzi. Then, was it Zhuangzi who dreamed that he was a butterfly, or was it a butterfly who dreamed that it was Zhuangzi?

3

Maybe Zhuangzi was the butterfly, and maybe the butterfly was Zhuangzi.

4

27

自然的箫声——庄子说 I

昔者庄周梦为胡蝶，栩栩然胡蝶也，自喻适志与！不知周也。俄然觉，则蘧蘧然周也。不知周之梦为胡蝶，胡蝶之梦为周与？周与胡蝶，则必有分矣。此之谓物化。

《庄子◎齐物论第二》

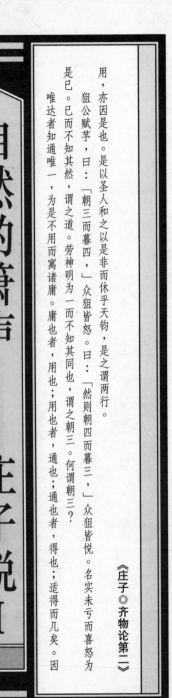

用，亦因是也。是以圣人和之以是非而休乎天钧，是之谓两行。

狙公赋芧，曰：「朝三而暮四，」众狙皆怒。曰：「然则朝四而暮三，」众狙皆悦。名实未亏而喜怒为用，谓之道。劳神明为一而不知其同也，谓之朝三。何谓朝三？

是已。已而不知其然，谓之道。

唯达者知通唯一，为是不用而寓诸庸。庸也者，用也；用也者，通也；通也者，得也；适得而几矣。因

《庄子◎齐物论第二》

Hui Shi Leans Against a Tree

1 Hui Shi was a man of great rhetorical skills, and he spent his life debating with others.

2 Victory! Defeat.

One day, while resting there, he suddenly realized the principle of not debating.

3 After a hard day's debating, he would prop himself up against a certain tree and rest.

4 After that he never debated with anyone ever again.

5 Can relying on rhetoric to defeat someone in a debate really be considered a victory? If you think so, then you've already been defeated.

昭文之鼓琴也，师旷之枝策也，惠子之据梧也，三子之知几乎，皆其盛者也，故载之末年。

自然的箫声——庄子说 I

29

Paoding Carves Up a Cow

One time, a butcher named Paoding was commissioned to butcher a cow for King Hui. As he worked, his movements were graceful and faultless. The sound of the knife between the bones was like a whisper in the night. When Paoding was finished, the cow didn't even know it was dead.

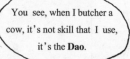

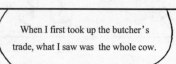

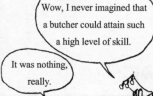

庖丁为文惠君解牛，手之所触，肩之所倚，足之所履，膝之所踦，砉然向然，奏刀騞然，莫不中音。合于桑林之舞，乃中经首之会。

文惠君曰：「嘻，善哉！技盖至此乎？」

庖丁释刀对曰：「臣之所好者道也，进乎技矣。始臣之解牛之时，所见无非全牛者。三年之后，未尝见全牛也。方今之时，臣以神遇而不以目视，官知止而神欲行。依乎天理，批大郄，导大窾，因其固然。技经

自然的箫吉——主子兑Ⅰ

5 But after I had been at it for a few years and butchered a good number of cows, what I saw was no longer the whole cow, but just it's skeletal structure. Ever since then, I stopped using my eyes and used my mind way around the cow.

6 The average cook goes trough a knife every month, because he hacks and chops.

7 The good cook changes knives every year, because he merely chops but doesn't hack.

8 Because I neither hack nor chop, I've used this same knife for nineteen years, and it's still like new.

Barely one month...

19 years.

9 My knife glides in and out between the bone joints, moving as it pleases; so, the cow suffers no pain and in the end, doesn't even know it's dead.

10 Fantastic! What you have said today has taught me a lot about how to live one's life.

The complexities of life are like the skeletal structure of the cow, and those who don't understand how to approach them end up running around in circles, wasting all their energy.

自然的箫声——庄子说Ⅰ

《庄子◎养生主第三》

文惠君曰：「善哉！吾闻庖丁之言，得养生焉。」

顾，为之踌躇满志，善刀而藏之。

虽然，每至于族，吾见其难为，怵然为戒，视为止，行为迟。动刀甚微，謋然已解，如土委地。提刀而立，为之四

彼节者有闲，而刀刃者无厚；以无厚入有闲，恢恢乎其于游刃必有余地矣，是以十九年而刀刃若新发于硎。

肯綮之未尝，而况大軱乎！良庖岁更刀，割也；族庖月更刀，折也。今臣之刀十九年矣，所解数千牛矣，而刀刃若新

Passing on the Flame

When oil is used to burn a flame, even though the oil may be burned up, the flame can be transferred to another fuel, and theoretically burn forever.

1

Our bodies will die someday, but our spirit and thoughts can be passed on, forever.

Dao

Dao

Dao

2

Self-cultivation is not aimed at preserving the body, but at nourishing the spirit, allowing it to live forever.

The Caged Chicken

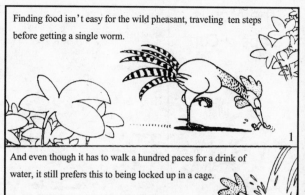
Finding food isn't easy for the wild pheasant, traveling ten steps before getting a single worm.

1

And even though it has to walk a hundred paces for a drink of water, it still prefers this to being locked up in a cage.

2

A caged chicken may have enough to eat and drink and it's feathers may be bright and shiny, but it will always crave the freedom of being on the outside.

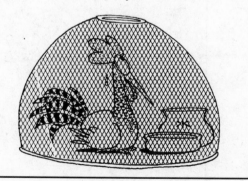

3

The person who understands self-cultivation would never pursue material pleasures at the expense of freedom, Yet in today's society, how many truly carefree people do you see?

泽雉十步一啄，百步一饮，不蕲畜乎樊中。神虽王，不善也。

自然的簫声——庄子说 I

《庄子◎养生主第三》

自然的箫声——庄子说 I

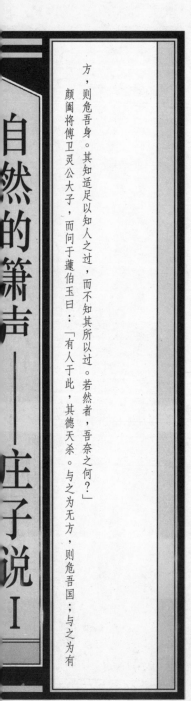

颜阖将傅卫灵公大子，而问于蘧伯玉曰：「有人于此，其德天杀。与之为无方，则危吾国；与之为有方，则危吾身。其知适足以知人之过，而不知其所以过。若然者，吾奈之何？

《庄子◎人间世第四》

平？怒其臂以当车辙，不知其不胜任也，是其才之美者也。戒之，慎之，积伐而美者以犯之，几矣。」之为婴儿；彼且为无町畦，亦与之为无町畦；彼且为无崖，亦与之为无崖。达之，入于无疵。汝不知夫螳螂入，和不欲出。形就而入，且为颠为灭，为崩为蹶。心和而出，且为声为名，为妖为孽。彼且为婴儿，亦与蘧伯玉曰：「善哉问乎！戒之，慎之，正女身也哉！形莫若就，心莫若和。虽然，之二者有患。就不欲

35

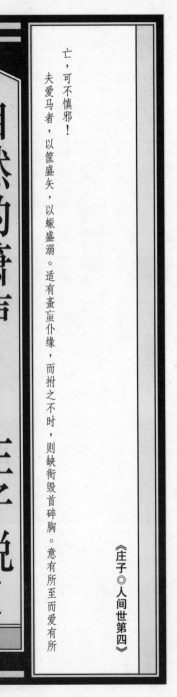

亡，可不慎邪！

夫爱马者，以筐盛矢，以蜄盛溺。适有蚊虻仆缘，而拊之不时，则缺衔毁首碎胸。意有所至而爱有所

《庄子◎人间世第四》

The Horse Lover

There was once a man who loved his horse so much that

1

He waited on it hand and foot. He used a wicker basket to catch the horse's droppings, and a huge conch shell to catch its urine.

2

One day, when the man went to slap a horsefly off his horse's backside,

3

4

The horse was startled and kicked the man, who died instantly from the blow.

You may love a person, but that person will not necessarily understand your love.

36

The Earth Spirit's Tree

1 A master carpenter was taking his students to the state of Qi to build a house.

2 On the way, they passed a tree standing beside a temple to the earth spirit. The tree was gigantic beyond compare. It's trunk was huge, and it was so tall that it almost touched the clouds.

3 Hmph!

4 Master!

5 Hey, that's the biggest tree we've ever seen. How come you didn't even stop and take a look?

6 Forget it. That thing is completely useless.

自然的箫声——庄子说 I

匠石之齐，至于曲辕，见栎社树。其大蔽数千牛，絜之百围，其高临山十仞而后有枝，其可以为舟者旁十数。观者如市，匠伯不顾，遂行不辍。弟子厌观之，走及匠石，曰：「自吾执斧斤以随夫子，未尝见材如此其美也。先生不肯视，行不辍，何邪？」曰：「已矣，勿言之矣！散木也，以为舟则沉，以为棺椁则速腐，以为器则速毁，以为门户则液樠，以为柱则蠹。是不材之木也，无所可用，故能若是之寿。」

自然的箫声——主子说 I

也，奈何哉其相物也？而几死之散人，又恶知散木！」

且子求无所可用久矣，几死，乃今得之，为予大用。使予也而有用，且得有此大也邪？且也若与予也皆物则辱；大枝折，小枝泄。此以其能若其生者也，故不终其天年而中道夭，自掊击于世俗者也。物莫不若是。

匠石归，栎社见梦曰：「女将恶乎比予哉？若将比予于文木邪？夫柤梨橘柚，果蓏之属，实熟则剥，剥

《庄子◎人间世第四》

A Tree's Natural Life Span

In Song, there was a place that was well suited for growing japonica, cypress, and mulberry trees. When these trees grew to a certain width, they were cut down and used to build monkey cages.

1

The thicker ones were used to build tall houses.

2

If even thicker, they were cut down and used to make coffins for the rich.

3

So, none of these trees ever lived to enjoy a full natural lifespan, and instead were cut down in the prime of life.

Those poor useful trees.

4

自然的箫声——庄子说 I

围，贵人富商之家求樿傍者斩之。故未终其天年，而中道之夭于斧斤，此材之患也。

宋有荆氏者，宜楸柏桑。其拱把而上者，求狙猴之杙者斩之；三围四围，求高名之丽者斩之；七围八

39

自然的簫声——庄子说Ⅰ

《庄子◎人间世第四》

神人之所以为大祥也。

故解之牛之白额者与豚之亢鼻者，与人有痔病者不可以适河。此皆巫祝以知之矣，所以为不祥也。此乃

In ancient times, during the sacrifice to the river god, the shaman would never choose a cow with a white forehead, a pig with a long snout, or a person with hemorrhoids to throw into the river as a sacrifice. They were considered to be "inauspicious". 5

a cow with a white forehead

Inauspicious creatures.

a person with hemorrhoids

a pig with a long snout

And the intelligent and versatile person would pretend to be unfit, or inauspicious, in order to avoid this spiritual disaster.

inauspicious

inauspicious

inauspicious

6

Beautiful and ugly each have their own special characteristics. It's not necessary to distinguish between "good" and "bad" and "auspicious" and "inauspicious"

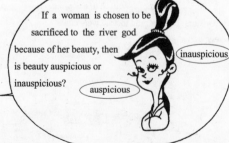

If a woman is chosen to be sacrificed to the river god because of her beauty, then is beauty auspicious or inauspicious?

inauspicious

auspicious

The Freak

1 There once was a very peculiar man named Zhi Lishu, whose body was terribly deformed. His head was bent down below his navel, shoulders reached up above the top of his head, hair stuck out in all directions, vital organs were all out of place, and stomach was down between his thighs.

2 By helping people with their laundry, Zhi lishu could make enough money to get by.

3 And by telling fortunes, he could support a dozen people.

Very lucky,

very lucky.

4 During times of war when people were conscripted by force, Zhi Lishu sauntered down the street knowing that nobody would want him.

Humby dee dum dum.

During times of famine when the government gave out free grain, Zhi Lishu would be first in line due to his disability.

rice

The wise person doesn't care about an unappealing aspect or disabilities. These attributes can also save one from much grief and hardship.

Right!

wine

自然的箫声——庄子说Ⅰ

《庄子◎人间世第四》

支离疏者，颐隐于脐，肩高于顶，食撮指天，五管在上，两髀为胁。挫针治繲，足以餬口；鼓筴播精，足以食十人。上征武士，则支离攘臂而游于其间；上有大役，则支离以有常疾不受功；上与病者粟，则受三钟与十束薪。夫支离其形者，犹足以养其身，终其天年，又况支离其德者乎！

41

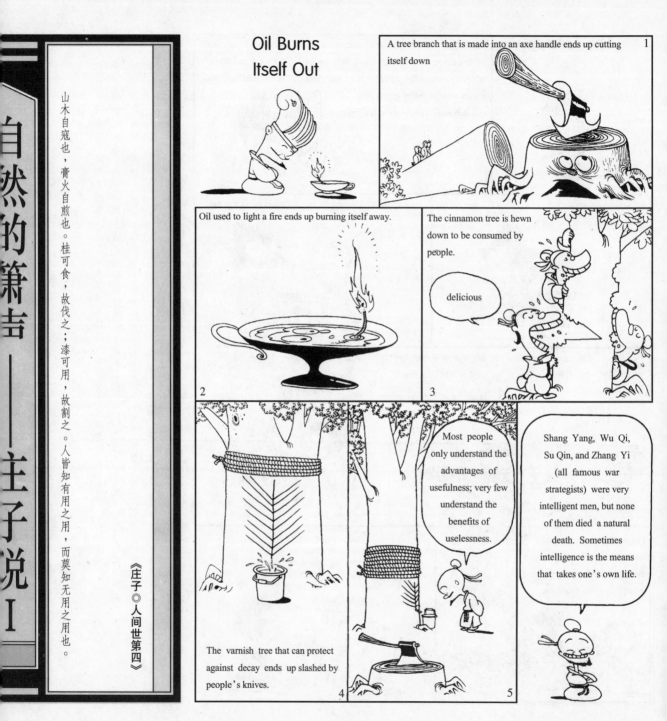

自然的箫吉——主子说 I

山木自寇也，膏火自煎也。桂可食，故伐之；漆可用，故割之。人皆知有用之用，而莫知无用之用也。

《庄子◎人间世第四》

Oil Burns Itself Out

A tree branch that is made into an axe handle ends up cutting itself down

Oil used to light a fire ends up burning itself away.

The cinnamon tree is hewn down to be consumed by people.

delicious

The varnish tree that can protect against decay ends up slashed by people's knives.

Most people only understand the advantages of usefulness; very few understand the benefits of uselessness.

Shang Yang, Wu Qi, Su Qin, and Zhang Yi (all famous war strategists) were very intelligent men, but none of them died a natural death. Sometimes intelligence is the means that takes one's own life.

The Tiger Trainer

饱，达其怒心。虎之与人异类而媚养己者，顺也；故其杀之之怒者，逆也。

汝不知夫养虎者乎？不敢以生物与之，为其杀之之怒也；不敢以全物与之，为其决之之怒也；时其饥

《庄子○人间世第四》

Training tigers is a very dangerous business. A person who understands the art of tiger training would never feed a tiger a live animal.

1

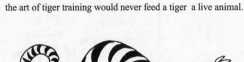

Because in the act of killing, a tiger becomes incensed,

2

And once its killing instincts are aroused, there's no turning back.

3

Therefore, the trainer always takes his animal's feelings into account

4

A tiger has feelings, too, and if they are attended to with care, instead of being fearsome, the tiger will be friendly.

And the fearsome tiger grows up as tame as a pussycat.

That's a good kitty

Meow

5

43

自然的箫声——庄子说Ⅰ

鲁有兀者叔山无趾，踵见仲尼。仲尼曰：「子不谨，前既犯患若是矣。虽今来，何及矣！」

无趾曰：「吾唯不知务而轻用吾身，吾是以亡足。今吾来也，犹有尊足者存，吾是以务全之也。夫天无不覆，地无不载，吾以夫子为天地，安知夫子之犹若是也！」

孔子曰：「丘则陋矣。夫子胡不入乎，请讲以所闻！」

无趾出。孔子曰：「弟子勉之！夫无趾，兀者也，犹务学以复补前行之恶，而况全德之人乎！」

《庄子◎德充符第五》

Toeless Shu

There once was a man in Lu by the name of Toeless Shu Shan. Toeless Shu had had his toes chopped off for committing a crime. — 1

One day, he walked on his stumps to go see confucius. — 2

3

It's because you didn't care about you're own well-being that you had your toes cut off. It's too late to change that now.

I may not have any toes, but the rest of my body is still here, and I came to you in the hope of preserving that. — 4

I apologize!

Hmph!

You are a wise man. Please come in and teach my disciples.

5

But Toeless Shu had already started on his way.

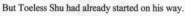
6

Toeless Shu Shan was a man of high virtue, and that is why Confucius changed his attitude toward him. A simple disability does not make one a cripple.

Nature the Superhero

Nature is like a superhero, its limitless strength continually pulsing.

1

Nature gave me my body;

2

Gave me vitality so that I can work hard;

3

Gave me age so that I can grow old in ease and comfort;

4

Gave me death so that I can have everlasting peace.

5

Nature is constantly changing, and people have to acknowledge and adapt to these changes. This way you won't always be fearful and angry, and the distinction between life and death will lose its significance.

自然的箫声——庄子说 I

道。

泉涸，鱼相与处于陆，相呴以湿，相濡以沫，不如相忘于江湖，与其誉尧而非桀也，不如两忘而化其

《庄子◎大宗师第六》

相忘乎江湖，人相忘乎道术。」

孔子曰：「鱼相造乎水，人相造乎道。相造乎水者，穿池而养给；相造乎道者，无事而生定。故曰，鱼

子贡曰：「敢问其方。」

孔子曰：「丘，天之戮民也。虽然，吾与汝共之。」

子贡曰：「然则夫子何方之依？」

《庄子◎大宗师第六》

Forgetting the Dao

Zi Gong asked Confucius:

1. Master, why do we have to live in the world and be bound by the rules of society?

2. If you want to live outside the world, that's fine, too.

How?

People are only comfortable living in the Dao.

Fish are only comfortable living in water.

道 Dao

3.

5. Free and unfettered in lakes and streams, fish forget that they live in water.

Fish live in water.

Satisfied and happy in nature, people forget about the existence of the Dao.

7. People live in the Dao!

道 Dao

We lose our carefree nature by separating our minds into cubicles and stuffing them full of knowledge. We should strive to transcend knowledge.

6. Water? What water?

Dao? What Dao?

道 Dao

8.

为之者而不得也。然而至此极者，命也夫！」

曰：「吾思夫使我至此极者而弗得也。父母岂欲吾贫哉？天无私覆，地无私载，天地岂私贫我哉？求其

子舆入，曰：「子之歌诗，何故若是？」

琴曰：「父邪！母邪！天乎！人乎！」有不任其声而趋举其诗焉。

子舆与子桑友，而霖雨十日。子舆曰：「子桑殆病矣！」裹饭而往食之。至子桑之门，则若歌若哭，鼓

《庄子◎大宗师第六》

47

行，确乎能其事者而已矣。且鸟高飞以避矰弋之害，鼷鼠深穴乎神丘之下以避熏凿之患，而曾二虫之无知！

狂接舆曰：「是欺德也；其于治天下也，犹涉海凿河而使蚉负山也。夫圣人之治也，治外乎？正而后

肩吾曰：「告我君人者以已出经式义度，人孰敢不听而化诸！」

肩吾见狂接舆，狂接舆曰：「日中始何以语女？」

《庄子◎应帝王第七》

Digging a Hole in the Ocean Floor

One day when Jian Wu went to see Kuang Jieyu, Kuang Jieyu asked:

What did Ri Zhongshi say to you?

He said only people who are regulated according to the legal and moral codes of man will submit and be civil.

1

I beg to differ. That method of governing is like trying to dig a hole in the ocean floor,

2

Or like telling a mosquito to carry a mountain on its back.

The laws of man are temporal, or at least transitional. If universal peace is to be achieved, we must follow the laws of nature, or the Dao.

3

Are a Duck's Legs Too Short?

1 Naturally long couldn't be too long, and short couldn't be too short.

2 Although a duck's legs are very short, it certainly wouldn't want them lengthened.

And although a crane's legs are very long, it'd be outraged if they were shortened.

3

A duck's legs are short, but its neck is long. **4**

Hee, hee, is it convenient?

5

And a crane's legs are long, while its neck is short. So in the end, everything is as it should be.

6

Try not to distinguish long and short according to the standard of man. Instead, observe their functions in nature, and you'll see that long is no longer long and short is no longer short.

自然的箫声——庄子说Ⅰ

何其多忧也？

短，续之则忧；鹤胫虽长，断之则悲。故性长非所断，性短非所续，无所去忧也。意仁义其非人情乎！彼仁人

彼正正者，不失其性命之情。故合者不为骈，而枝者不为跂；长者不为有余，短者不为不足。是故凫胫虽

枝之道，非天下之至正也。

骈于辩者，累瓦结绳窜句，游心于坚白同异之闲，而敝跬誉无用之言非乎？而杨墨是已。故此皆多骈旁

《庄子◎骈拇第八》

49

自然的箫声——主子兑 I

羊。问臧奚事，则挟策读书；问榖奚事，则博塞以游。二人者，事业不同，其于亡羊均也。

身殉天下。故此数子者，事业不同，名声异号，其于伤性以身为殉，一也。臧与榖，二人相与牧羊而俱亡其

自三代以下者，天下莫不以物易其性矣，小人则以身殉利，士则以身殉名，大夫则以身殉家，圣人则以

《庄子◎骈拇第八》

The Lost Goat

50

Thieves Have Principles, Too

1

Once upon a time, there was a notorious thief named Dao Zhi.

Excuse me, I have a question...

2

Of course we do!

Do we thieves have principles, too?

Being able to find out where hidden treasure is, is called **Sagacity**.

Gold!

3

When robbing a house, going in first is called **Courage**.

I'll go in first and take a look around.

4

After a robbery, coming out last is called **Chivalry**.

You guys go ahead, I'll take up the rear.

5

自然的箫声——庄子说Ⅰ

故跖之徒问于跖曰：「盗亦有道乎？」跖曰：「何适而无有道邪！」夫妄意室中之藏，圣也；入先，勇也；出后，义也；知可否，知也；分均，仁也。五者不备而能成大盗者，天下未之有也。由是观之，善人不得圣人之道不立，跖不得圣人之道不行；天下之善人少而不善人多，则圣人之利天下也少而害天下也多。

51

故跖之徒问于跖曰：「盗亦有道乎？」跖曰：「何适而无有道邪！」夫妄意室中之藏，圣也；入先，勇也；出后，义也；知可否，知也；分均，仁也。五者不备而能成大盗者，天下未之有也。由是观之，善人不得圣人之道不立，跖不得圣人之道不行；天下之善人少而不善人多，则圣人之利天下也少而害天下也多。

《庄子◎胠箧第十》

自然的箫声——庄子说 I

《庄子◎胠箧第十》

怒，乃以赵厚酒易鲁薄酒，奏之。楚王以赵酒薄，故围邯郸也。

许慎注淮南云：楚会诸侯，鲁赵俱献酒于楚王。鲁酒薄而赵酒厚，楚之主酒过求酒于赵，赵不与。吏

而谷虚，丘夷而渊实。圣人已死，则大盗不起，天下平而无故矣。

故曰，唇竭则齿寒，鲁酒薄而邯郸围，圣人生而大盗起。掊击圣人，纵舍盗贼，而天下始治矣。夫川竭

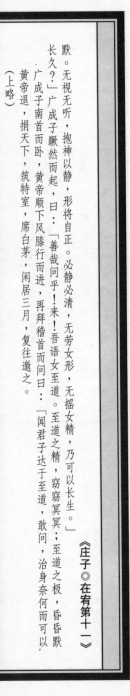

自然为箴言 庄子说

（上略）

默。无视无听，抱神以静，形将自正。必静必清，无劳女形，无摇女精，乃可以长生。

长久？」广成子蹶然而起，曰：「善哉问乎！来！吾语女至道：至道之精，窈窈冥冥；至道之极，昏昏默

广成子南首而卧，黄帝顺下风膝行而进，再拜稽首而问曰：「闻君子达于至道，敢问，治身奈何而可以

黄帝退，捐天下，筑特室，席白茅，闲居三月，复往邀之。

《庄子◎在宥第十一》

The Emperor Goes to Guang Chengzi

1 When the emperor had been reigning for nineteen years and had brought peace and prosperity to the land, he heard about an enlightened master named Guang Chengzi.

2 I want to use the vitality of nature to harmonize the Yin and the Yang, this will bring unprecedented harvests. I want to stabilize the lives of my people...

You say you want to use the vitality of the Dao to enhance the natural processes? This will only destroy them. Don't you understand that to use our intellect to change things only makes matters worse?

Out of curiosity, the emperor went to see him.

3 Upon hearing this, the king's passion turned to dust and he immediately abdicated. He left the world behind and went to live by himself in a grass hut. He stayed there in peace and solitude for three months.

4

5 What can I do to live a long life?

The Dao is chaotic, neither bright nor dark.

6 Don't see with your eyes, Don't hear with your ears, Don't think with your mind, Embrace the primal one, No knowledge, no self, Go with nature, Participate in nature, be one with nature, And a long life will come naturally.

54

Nature's Friend

1 There is a kind of sage who emulates the wisdom of nature. His teaching methods are like the relationship of a form and its shadow.

2 Where there's a question, there's an answer; where there's and action, there's a reaction.

... a sound and its echo.

HELLO!
HELLO!

3 Because body and spirit are in harmony. When he is at rest, there is no sound.

4 When he moves, he leaves no trace. Therefore, he is able to bring those who are muddled and confused back to the natural Dao.

5 Those people who believe that one's body is the temple of one's soul may well enough be good people, but the person who is able to go beyond his corporeal form is the true companion of nature.

Only the selfless person can live up to the standards of nature because your body is just one temporary form in nature's constantly changing process.Selfishness is trying to hang on to what you have.

自然的箫声——庄子说 I

者，昔之君子，睹无者，天地之友。

复之挠挠，以游无端；出入无旁，与日无始；颂论形躯，合乎大同，大同而无己。无己，恶乎得有有！睹有

大人之教，若形之于影，声之于响。有问而应之，尽其所怀，为天下配。处乎无响，行乎无方。挈汝适

百姓而已哉！出入六合，游乎九州，独往独来，是谓独有。独有之人，是谓至贵。

夫有土者，有大物也。有大物者，不可以物；物而不物，故能物物。明乎物物者之非物也，岂独治天下

《庄子◎在宥第十一》

55

自然的箫声——庄子说 I

桓公曰：「寡人读书，轮人安得议乎！有说则可，无说则死。」

轮扁曰：「臣也以臣之事观之。斲轮，徐则甘而不固，疾则苦而不入。不徐不疾，得之于手而应于心，口不能言，有数存焉于其间。臣不能以喻臣之子，臣之子亦不能受之于臣，是以行年七十而老斲轮。古之人与其不可传也死矣，然则君之所读者，古人之糟魄已夫！」

《庄子◎天道第十三》

自然的箴言——庄子说 I

天其运乎？地其处乎？日月其争于所乎？孰主张是？孰维纲是？孰居无事推而行事？意者其有机缄而不得已邪？意者其运转而不能自止邪？云者为雨乎？雨者为云乎？孰隆施是？孰居无事淫乐而劝是？风起北方，一西一东，有上彷徨，孰嘘吸是？孰居无事而披拂是？敢问何故？

《庄子◎天运第十四》

Crows and Seagulls

1 One day, Confucius dropped in on Laozi to discuss benevolence and justice.

2 In the course of the conversation, Laozi said: Seagulls don't become white by washing themselves every day.

3 And crows don't become black by dipping themselves in ink every day.

INK

4 Black and white are both natural characteristics. So you can't say one is better than the other.

White is beautiful!

Black is beautiful!

Gimme a break!

5 To a person who understands the Dao, when you use benevolence and justice to distinguish between good and evil, you're making the same mistake.

自然的箫声　庄子说Ⅰ

孔子见老聃而语仁义。老聃曰：「夫播穅眯目，则天地四方易位矣；蚊虻噆肤，则通昔不寐矣。夫仁义潜然乃愤吾心，乱莫大焉。吾子使天下无失其朴，吾子亦放风而动，总德而立矣，又奚杰然若负建鼓而求亡子者邪？夫鹄不日浴而白，乌不日黔而黑。黑白之朴，不足以为辩；名誉之观，不足以为广。」

《庄子◎天运第十四》

59

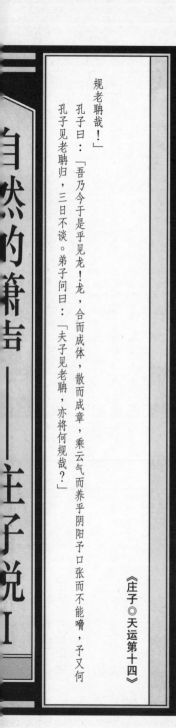

規老聃哉！」

孔子曰：「吾乃今于是乎見龍！龍，合而成体，散而成章，乘云气而养乎阴阳予口张而不能嗋，予又何

孔子見老聃归，三日不谈。弟子问曰：「夫子見老聃，亦将何規哉？」

《庄子◎天运第十四》

Confucius Sees a Dragon

1 After his meeting with Laozi, Confucius returned home and didn't speak for three days.

2 Master, when you went to see Laozi what did you teach him?

Um, um, um

Confucius knew that Laozi understood the way of nature—ceaseless transformation. When facing a person who understands the Dao, words are useless and unnecessary.

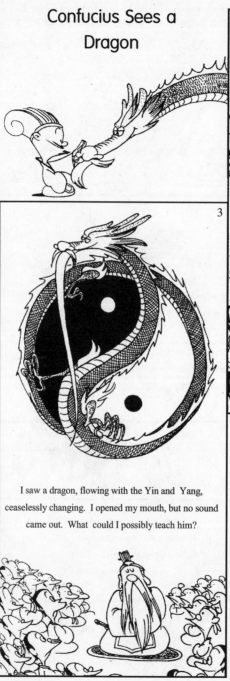

3 I saw a dragon, flowing with the Yin and Yang, ceaselessly changing. I opened my mouth, but no sound came out. What could I possibly teach him?

Don't Ring the Bull's Nose

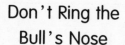

1

One day, Hebo asked the sea spirit:

> What is natural and what is man-made?

2

Four legs on horses and cows is natural.

3

A horse's harness,

4

and a bull's nose ring are man-made.

> Man-made knowledge, morality, and laws all work against nature, just like a horse's harness and a bull's nose ring.

自然的箫声——庄子说Ⅰ

故曰，无以人灭天，无以故灭命，无以得殉名。谨守而勿失，是谓反其真。

北海若曰：「牛马四足，是谓天；落马首，穿牛鼻，是谓人。

河伯曰：「何谓天？何谓人？」

《庄子◎秋水第十七》

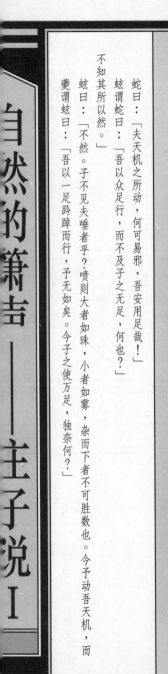

蛇曰：「夫天机之所动，何可易邪，吾安用足哉！」

蚿谓蛇曰：「吾以众足行，而不及子之无足，何也？」

不知其所以然。

蚿曰：「不然。子不见夫唾者乎？喷则大者如珠，小者如雾，杂而下者不可胜数也。今予动吾天机，而

夔谓蚿曰：「吾以一足趻踔而行，予无如矣。今子之使万足，独奈何？」

The Wind and the Snake

62

自然的箫声——庄子说I

屋者，唯我能也，故以众小不胜为大胜也。为大胜者，唯圣人能之。」

风曰：「然。予蓬蓬然起于北海而入于南海也，然而指我则胜我，鳅我亦胜我。虽然，夫折大木，蜚大屋者，唯我能也，故以众小不胜为大胜也。为大胜者，唯圣人能之。」

蛇谓风曰：「予动吾脊胁而行，则有似也。今子蓬蓬然起于北海，蓬蓬然入于南海，而似无有，何也？」

《庄子◎秋水第十七》

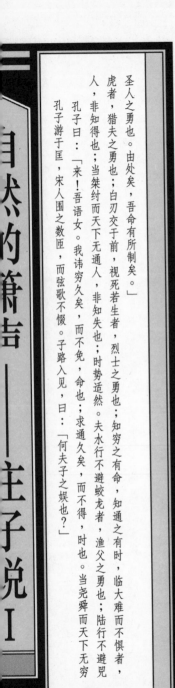

圣人之勇也。由处矣，吾命有所制矣。」

虎者，猎夫之勇也；白刃交于前，视死若生者，烈士之勇也；知穷之有命，知通之有时，临大难而不惧者，人，非知得也；当桀纣而天下无通人，非知失也；时势适然。夫水行不避蛟龙者，渔父之勇也；陆行不避兕

孔子曰：「来！吾语女。我讳穷久矣，而不免，命也；求通久矣，而不得，时也。当尧舜而天下无穷

孔子游于匡，宋人围之数匝，而弦歌不惙。子路入见，曰：「何夫子之娱也？」

1 One day when Confucius was on a journey with his disciples in Zhou, he was surrounded by a posse who mistook him for the criminal Yang Hu.

2 Don't panic, just sit still and continue listening to me teach.

But aren't you afraid, Master?

Of course I am, Zhong You, but listen...

Not to fear water dragons is the courage of the fisherman.

64

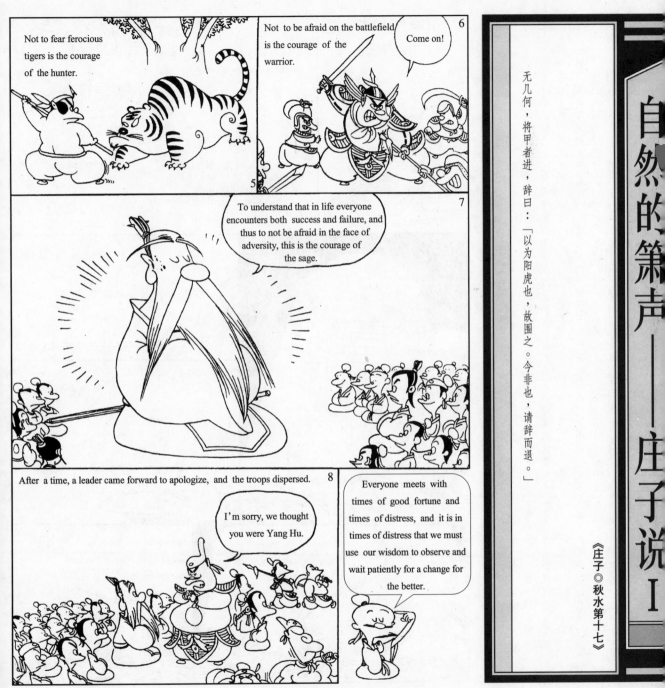

公孫龍問于魏牟曰：「龍少學先生之道，長而明仁義之行；合同異，離堅白；然不然，可不可；困百家之知，窮眾口之辯；吾自以為至達已。今吾聞莊子之言，汒焉異之。不知論之不及與，知之弗若與？今吾無所開吾喙，敢問其方。」

公子牟隱机大息，仰天而笑曰：「子獨不聞夫坎井之蛙乎？謂東海之鱉曰：『吾樂與！出跳梁乎井幹之上，入休乎缺甃之崖；赴水則接腋持頤，蹶泥則沒足滅跗；還虷蟹與科斗，莫吾能若也。且夫擅一壑之水，

The Frog in the Well

1
One day, sidling up from the ocean, a tortoise passed by a well.

well

2
Hey, come on in and sit for a while.

3
Do you live in this well?

4
Sure! And I live like a king here!

5
When I leap into the water, it supports my weight and keeps me afloat.

6
And when I dive below the surface, I relax and let the mud massage my legs.

自然的箫声——庄子说I

之，适适然惊，规规然自失也。之时八年七旱，而崖不为加损。夫不为顷久推移，不以多少进退者，此亦东海之大乐也。』于是埳井之蛙闻告之海曰：『夫千里之远，不足以举其大；千仞之高，不足以极其深。禹之时十年九潦，而水弗为加益；汤而跨跱坎井之乐，此亦至矣，夫子奚不时来入观乎！』东海之鳖左足未入，而右膝已絷矣。于是逡巡而却，之，适适然惊，规规然自失也。

子之故，失子之业。」

子往矣！且子独不闻夫寿陵余子之学行于邯郸与？未得国能，又失其故行矣，直匍匐而归耳。今子不去，将忘子之业，失

东无西，始于玄冥，反于大通。子乃规规然而求之以察，索之以辩，是直用管窥天，用锥指地也，不亦小乎！

极妙之言而自适一时之利者，是非坎井之蛙与？且彼方跳黄泉而登大皇，无南无北，奭然四解，沦于不测；无

且夫知不知是非之竟，而犹欲观于庄子之言，是犹使蚊虻负山，商蚷驰河也，必不胜任矣。且夫知不知论

《庄子◎秋水第十七》

If you want to talk big, the Eastern Sea is big.

Bigger than my well?

13

The Eastern Sea is so big, that a thousand miles isn't enough to measure the distance across, and a thousand yards isn't enough to measure its depth.

14

15

You know, there was a time long, long ago, when nine years out of ten, there were continuous rain and floods, yet the Eastern Sea didn't get any bigger.

16

And another time, seven years out of eight, there was a continuous drought, and yet the Eastern Sea didn't get any smaller.

Liar!

Now that is big. Your well is nothing in comparison.

The frog was limited by his well just like people are limited by knowledge. Knowledge can make us great, but it can also make us small; so we have to go beyond mere knowledge.

17

There was once a little boy in Yan who went to the city Handan to learn how to walk like the people there.

1

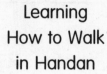

?

2

But not only did he not learn how to walk there, he forgot how to walk altogether!

3

Ah! I can't walk!

4

So he had to crawl home.

At the outset, people who study are in search of the essence of nature, but after a while, they get lost in the forest of books and can't get out.

5

自然的箫声——庄子说 I

且子独不闻夫寿陵余子之学行于邯郸与？未得国能，又失其故行矣，直匍匐而归耳。

《庄子◎秋水第十七》

69

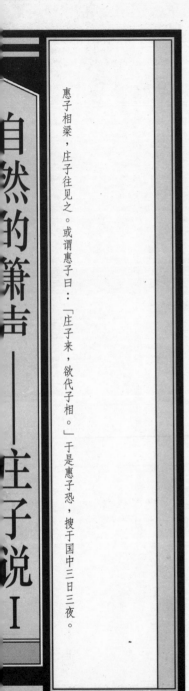

自然的簫聲——莊子說 I

惠子相梁，莊子往見之。或謂惠子曰：「莊子來，欲代子相。」於是惠子恐，搜於國中三日三夜。

A Crow Eating a Dead Rat

One day, Zhuangzi went to see Huizi, who was then prime minister of the Liang State.

1

Zhuangzi says that he is just coming for a friendly visit, but he really wants to take your place as prime minister.

2

!

3

Let's get down to brass tacks here, Zhuangzi. Just why did you come?

4

Huizi, have you ever heard of a southern bird called the phoenix? When the phoenix migrates from the Southern Sea to the Northern Sea, he rests only on the luxurious firmiana tree...

自然的簫聲——莊子說 I

《莊子◎秋水第十七》

非练实不食，非醴泉不饮。于是鸱得腐鼠，鹓鶵过之，仰而视之曰：『吓！』今子欲以子之梁国而吓我邪？』

庄子往见之，曰："南方有鸟，其名为鹓鶵，子知之乎？夫鹓鶵，发于南海而飞于北海，非梧桐不止，

《庄子◎秋水第十七》

自然的箫声——主子说Ⅰ

庄子与惠子游于濠梁之上。庄子曰：「鲦鱼出游从容，是鱼之乐也。」

惠子曰：「子非鱼，安知鱼之乐？」

庄子曰：「子非我，安知我不知鱼之乐？」

惠子曰：「我非子，固不知子矣；子固非鱼也，子之不知鱼之乐，全矣。」

庄子曰：「请循其本。子曰『汝安知鱼乐』云者，既已知吾知之而问我，我知之濠上也。」

Zhuangzi Dreams of a Skeleton

1 One day on his way to Chu, Zhuangzi happened upon a human skeleton.

2 Did you die from poverty? Or were you hacked to pieces when your country was conquered? Or did you implicate your parents in some horrible crime and commit suicide out of shame?

3 Did you starve to death? Did you freeze to death? Or were you old and just lay down here to die?

4 Night fell, and Zhuangzi lay down to sleep, using the skull as his pillow.

5 From listening to you talk today, you sound like a real rhetorician.

自然的箫声——庄子说 I

庄子之楚，见空髑髅，髐然有形，撽以马捶，因而问之，曰：「夫子贪生失理，而为此乎？将子有亡国之事，斧钺之诛，而为此乎？将子有不善之行，愧遗父母妻子之丑，而为此乎？将子有冻馁之患，而为此乎？将子之春秋故及此乎？」于是语卒，援髑髅，枕而卧。夜半，髑髅见梦曰：「子之谈者似辩士。视子所言，皆生人之累也，死则无此矣。子欲闻死之说乎？」

自然的讴吉
——主子兑Ⅰ

庄子曰：「然。」

髑髅曰：「死，无君于上，无臣于下；亦无四时之事，从然以天地为春秋，虽南面王乐，不能过也。」

庄子不信，曰：「吾使司命复生子形，为子骨肉肌肤，反子父母妻子间里知识，子欲之乎？」

髑髅深矉蹙頞曰：「吾安能弃南面王乐而复为人间之劳乎！」

《庄子◎至乐第十八》

自然的箫声——庄子说Ⅰ

昔者海鸟止于鲁郊，鲁侯御而觞之于庙，奏九韶以为乐，具太牢以为膳。鸟乃眩视忧悲，不敢食一脔，不敢饮一杯，三日而死。此以己养养鸟也，非以鸟养养鸟也。夫以鸟养养鸟者，宜栖之深林，游之坛陆，浮之江湖，食之鳅鲦，随行列而止，委蛇而处。彼唯人言之恶闻，奚以夫诧诧为乎！咸池九韶之乐，张之洞庭之

自然的箫吉——主子兑Ⅰ

相与异，其好恶故异也。故先圣不一其能，不同其事。名止于实，义设于适，是之谓条达而福持。鱼处水而生，人处水而死，彼必野，鸟闻之而飞，兽闻之而走，鱼闻之而下入，人卒闻之，相与还而观之。

《庄子◎至乐第十八》

5
This is all for you. Go ahead and dig in.

6
Drink up!

This is the best wine around!

7
After three days of neither eating nor drinking, the yuanju up and died.

8
Why didn't you eat? I gave you all of the best.

What some people believe to be the best music and the best food aren't necessarily so for everyone. Raise a bird according to a bird's wants, not a person's. The saying, "Do unto others as you would have others do unto you" is never really applicable.

自然的箫声——庄子说 I

庄子行于山中，见大木，枝叶盛茂，伐木者止其旁而不取也。问其故，曰：「无所可用。」庄子曰：

「此木以不材得终其天年。」

夫子出于山，舍于故人之家。故人喜，命竖子杀雁而烹之。竖子请曰：「其一能鸣，其一不能鸣，请奚杀？」主人曰：「杀不能鸣者。」

明日，弟子问于庄子曰：「昨日山中之木，以不材得终其天年；今主人之雁，以不材死；先生将何处？」

Riding with Nature

Dao

78

自然的箫吉——主子兑Ⅰ

孔子围于陈蔡之间，七日不火食。大公任往吊之曰：「子几死乎？」曰：「然。」「子恶死乎？」曰：「然。」任曰：「予尝言不死之道。东海有鸟焉，其名曰意怠。其为鸟也，翂翂翐翐，而似无能；引援而飞，迫胁而栖；进不敢为前，退不敢为后；食不敢先尝，必取其绪。是故其行列不斥，而外人卒不得害，是以免于

5. When resting, it huddles in the middle of the flock...

6. And when feeding, it doesn't compete for food. Therefore, nobody ever tries to hurt it.

Straight trees get cut down first, and it's the sweet spring water that is drunk first.

7.

8. You, on the other hand, seem to be using the brightness of your wisdom to show up other peoples faults. Of course people won't accept you for it!

Confucius was much enlightened by this and subsequently took leave of his friends and disciples to live alone in the forest and study the Dao.

9.

Don't show off your wisdom, or others will fear and resent you for it.

自然的箫声——庄子说Ⅰ

《庄子◎山木第二十》

兽不恶，而况人乎！

孔子曰：「善哉！」辞其交游，去其弟子，逃于大泽；衣裘褐，食杼栗，入兽不乱群，入鸟不乱行。鸟不恶，而况人乎！

孔子曰：「善哉！」辞其交游，去其弟子，逃于大泽；衣裘褐，食杼栗，入兽不乱群，入鸟不乱行。鸟不名处；纯纯常常，乃比于狂；削迹捐势，不为功名，是故无责于人，人亦无责焉。至人不闻，子何喜哉？」

闻之大成之人曰：『自伐者无功，功成者堕，名成者亏。』孰能去功与名而还与众人！道流而不明，居得而不名，乃比于狂；削迹捐势，不为功名，是故无责于人，人亦无责焉。至人不闻，子何喜哉？」

患。直木先伐，甘井先竭。子其意者饰知以惊愚，修身以明污，昭昭乎如揭日月而行，故不免也。昔吾

81

自然的箫吉——主子兑Ⅰ

穷祸患害相弃也；以天属者，迫穷祸患害相收也。夫相收之与相弃亦远矣。

赤子之累多矣；弃千金之璧，负赤子而趋，何也？」林回曰：「彼以利合，此以天属也。」夫以利合者，迫

子独不闻假人之亡兴？林回弃千金之璧，负赤子而趋。或曰：「为其布与？赤子之布寡矣；为其累与？

《庄子◎山木第二十》

Lin Hui Forsakes a Fortune

1 When the state of Chu was being conquered...

2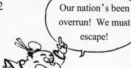

Our nation's been overrun! We must escape!

3

Forget it! Let's go!

4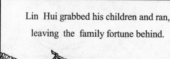

Lin Hui grabbed his children and ran, leaving the family fortune behind.

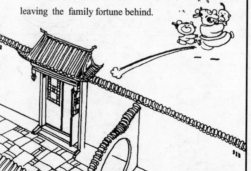

What is gained by assessing cost and benefit is lost in the same way. In a war-stricken world, there are fortunes to be made, but a loving parent sees avoiding danger as the highest priority.

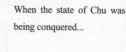

自然的箫声——庄子说 I

《庄子◎山木第二十》

仲尼曰：「始用四达，爵禄并至而不穷，物之所利，乃非己也，吾命其在外者也。君子不为盗，贤人不

而袭诸人间，社稷存焉尔。」

为窃。吾若取之，何哉！故曰，鸟莫知于鹢鸬，目之所不宜处，不给视，虽落其实，弃之而走。其畏人也，

「何谓无受人益难？」

83

自然的箫声——庄子兑 I

庄周游于雕陵之樊，睹一异鹊自南方来者，翼广七尺，目大运寸，感周之颡而集于栗林。庄周曰：「此何鸟哉，翼殷不逝，目大不睹？」蹇裳躩步，执弹而留之。睹一蝉，方得美荫而忘其身；螳螂执翳而搏之，见得而忘其形；异鹊从而利之，见利而忘其真。庄周怵然曰：「噫！物固相累，二类相召也！」捐弹而反走，虞人逐而谇之。

庄周反入，三日不庭。蔺且从而问之：「夫子何为顷间甚不庭乎？」

84

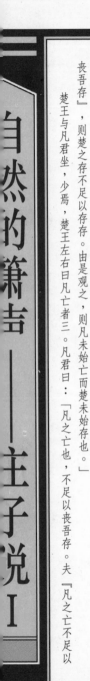

《庄子◎田子方第二十一》

丧吾存」，则楚之存不足以存存。由是观之，则凡未始亡而楚未始存也。」

楚王与凡君坐，少焉，楚王左右曰凡亡者三。凡君曰：「凡之亡也，不足以丧吾存。夫『凡之亡不足以

86

自然的箫声——庄子说Ⅰ

知不得问，反于帝宫，见黄帝而问焉。黄帝曰：「无思无虑始知道，无处无服始安道，无从无道始得道。」

狂屈曰：「唉！予所欲言。」

知不得问，反于白水之南，登狐阕之上，而睹狂屈焉。知以之言也问乎狂屈。

道？何处何服则安道？何从何道则得道？」三问而无为谓不答也，非不答，不知答也。

知北游于玄水之上，登隐弅之丘，而适遭无为谓焉。知谓无为谓曰：「予欲有问乎若：何思何虑则知

87

自然的箫吉——主子说Ⅰ

知问黄帝曰：「我与若知之，彼与彼不知也，其孰是邪？」

黄帝曰：「彼无为谓真是也，狂屈似之；我与汝终不近也。夫知者不言，言者不知，故圣人行不言之

教。道不可致，德不可至。仁可为也，义可亏也，礼相伪也。故曰，「失道而后德，失德而后仁，失仁而后

义，失义而后礼。礼者，道之华而乱之首也。」故曰，「为道者日损，损之又损之以至于无为，无为而无不

为也。」今已为物也，欲复归根，不亦难乎！其易也，其唯大人乎！

《庄子◎知北游第二十二》

Geng Sangchu Forsakes Fame

Geng Sangchu was a very adept student of Laozi.

1

2

While he was living on a cliff overlooking the village of Wei Lei, harvest time came around and the villagers had a bumper crop. They attributed their good fortune to Geng Sangchu overseeing them and so began to worship and give thanks to him. Geng Sangchu said to his disciples:

3

In the Springtime, leaves begin to grow and flowers blossom.

In the late Summer, plants come to fruition. It's the course of nature! But people say I am responsible for it just because I live up here. They think I am some kind of saint.

4

5

Thereupon, Geng Sangchu moved away to the forest.

垒之细民而窃窃焉欲俎豆予于贤人之间，我其杓之人邪！吾是以不释于老聃之言。」

宝成。夫春与秋，岂无得而然哉？天道已行矣。吾闻至人，尸居环堵之室，而百姓猖狂不知所如往。今以畏

庚桑子闻之，南面而不释然。弟子曰：「弟子何异于子？夫春气发而百草生，正得秋而万

计之而不足，岁计之而有余。庶几其圣人乎！子胡不相与尸而祝之，社而稷之乎？」

拥肿之与居，鞅掌之为使。居三年，畏垒大壤。畏垒之民相与言曰：「庚桑楚之始来，吾洒然异之，今吾日

老聃之役有庚桑楚者，偏得老聃之道，以北居畏垒之山，其臣之画然知者去之，其妾之挈然仁者远之；

《庄子◎庚桑楚第二十三》

89

自然的箫声——主子说 I

黄帝曰：「异哉小童！非徒知具茨之山，又知大隗之所存。请问为天下。」

「若知大隗之所存乎？」曰：「然。」

适遇牧马童子，问涂焉，曰：「若知具茨之山乎？」曰：「然。」

皆迷，无所问涂。

黄帝将见大隗平具茨之山，方明为御，昌寓骖乘，张若谄朋前马，昆阍滑稽后车；至于襄城之野，七圣

自然的箫声——庄子说 I

黄帝再拜稽首，称天师而退。

天下者，亦奚以异乎牧马者哉！亦去其害马者而已矣！」

黄帝曰：「夫为天下者，则诚非吾子之事。虽然，请问为天下。」小童辞。黄帝又问。小童曰：「夫为天下者，亦若此而已矣，又奚事焉！予少而自游于六合之内，予适有瞀病，有长者教予曰：『若乘日之车而游于襄城之野。』今予病少痊，予又且复游于六合之外。夫为天下亦若此而已，予又奚事焉！」

《庄子◎徐无鬼第二十四》

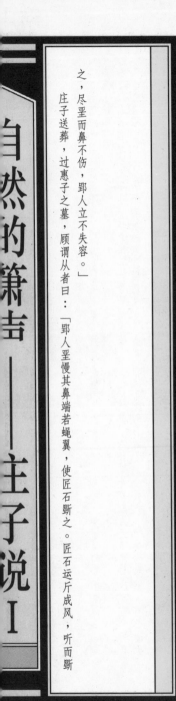

自然的箫吉——主子说Ⅰ

之，尽垩而鼻不伤，郢人立不失容。」

庄子送葬，过惠子之墓，顾谓从者曰：「郢人垩慢其鼻端若蝇翼，使匠石斲之。匠石运斤成风，听而斲

The Stone Mason and the Ying Man

1 After Huizi passed away Zhuangzi missed him very much.

Huizi

2 Once there was a citizen of the city of Ying who was patching up a building when a little bit of lime as thin as a fly's wing dripped down on to his nose.

3 Hey, can you help me chop off this little bit of lime?

4 Ready!
Ready?

6 The man from Ying stood still as the blow came, and the lime was cut away without the slightest harm to his nose.

Perfect!

5

92

夫子之死也，吾无以为质矣，吾无与言之矣。

「宋元君闻之，召匠石曰：『尝试为寡人为之。』匠石曰：『臣则尝能斲之。虽然，臣之质死久矣。』自

自然的箫吾——主子兑 I

客出而君惝然若有亡也。

曰：「通达之中有魏，于魏中有梁，于梁中有王，王与蛮氏，有辩乎？」君曰：「无辩。」

曰：「臣请为君实之。君以意在四方上下有穷乎？」君曰：「无穷。」……

君曰：「噫！其虚言与？」

「有国于蜗之左角者曰触氏，有国于蜗之右角者曰蛮氏，时相与争地而战，伏尸数万，逐北旬有五日而后反。」

《庄子◎则阳第二十五》

---

1 Not long after the kings of Wei and Qi formed an alliance, the king of Ji reneged, angering the king of Wei.

Attack Qi!

!

2 Your Majesty, one moment, please... Certainly you have heard of a tiny animal called the snail.

Of course!

3 Well, once there was a man named Chu who built a country on a snail's antenna. Then, on the other antenna of the same snail, a man named Man established his own nation. These two countries constantly fought over land, and in the process, countless people were killed.

Man   Chu

4 This is ridiculous! What are you getting at?!

5 Your Majesty, has all of the world's land been claimed already?

6 No, no, still quite a bit actually.

Once there was a country named Wei. And in the country of Wei, there was a city called Liang. And in the city of Liang, there was a palace. And in the palace there was a king. Is there really any difference between that king and the Chu and Man nations on the snail's antennae?

7 To one who understands he Dao, people who fight over land or other supposedly valuable things are like the nations fighting over the snail's antennae.

Zhuangzi Borrows Grain

自然的箫声——庄子说Ⅰ

《庄子◎外物第二十六》

庄周家贫，故往贷粟于监河侯。监河侯曰：「诺。我将得邑金，将贷子三百金，可乎？」

庄周忿然作色曰：「周昨来，有中道而呼者。周顾视车辙中，有鲋鱼焉。周问之曰：『鲋鱼来！子何为者邪？』对曰：『我，东海之波臣也。君岂有斗升之水而活我哉？』周曰：『诺。我且南游吴越之王，激西江之水而迎子，可乎？』鲋鱼忿然作色曰：『吾失我常与，我无所处。吾得斗升之水然活耳，君乃言此，曾不如早索我于枯鱼之肆！』」

95

自然的簫声 —— 主子兑 I

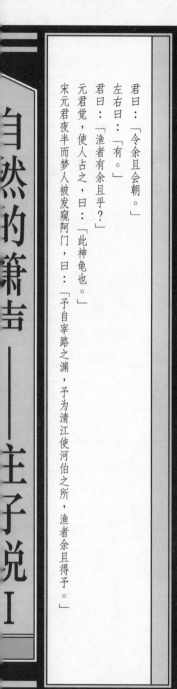

君曰：「令余且会朝。」
左右曰：「有。」
君曰：「渔者有余且乎？」
元君觉，使人占之，曰：「此神龟也。」
宋元君夜半而梦人被发窥阿门，曰：「予自宰路之渊，予为清江使河伯之所，渔者余且得予。」

The Turtle That Could Predict the Future

《庄子◎外物第二十六》

惠子谓庄子曰：「子言无用。」

庄子曰：「知无用而始可与言用矣。天地非不广且大也，人之所用容足耳。然则厕足而垫之致黄泉，人尚有用

乎？」

惠子曰：「无用。」

庄子曰：「然则无用之为用也亦明矣。」

自然的箫吉——主子说 I

Natural Use

One day, Zhuangzi lectured Huizi hour upon hour about the Dao.

1

Trivial! Inconsequential!

Everything you've said is completely useless!

2

3

Good. Now that you understand uselessness, we can talk about usefulness.

For instance, you're really only using this little piece of ground your standing on, right?

4

Ahhh!

6

Therefore: Usefulness is built on a foundation of uselessness. If there is no uselessness, then there is no usefulness.

But, if we cut away all the rest of the ground around it...

5

How useful is it?

7

useful

USELESS USELESS USELESS USELESS USELESS

After Catching the Fish, Discard the Trap

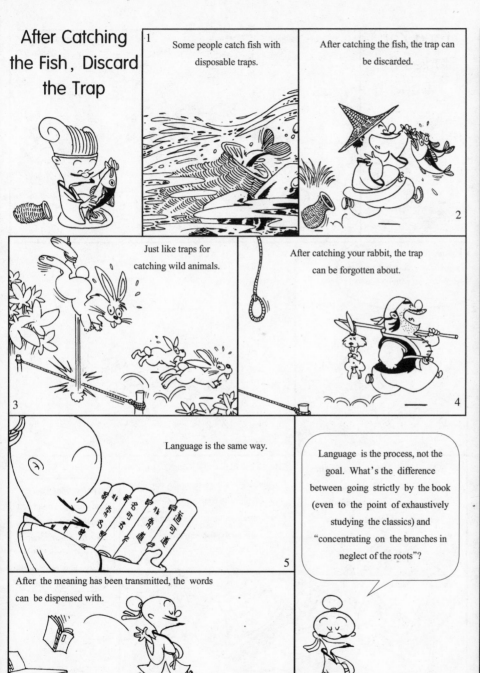

1 Some people catch fish with disposable traps.

2 After catching the fish, the trap can be discarded.

3 Just like traps for catching wild animals.

4 After catching your rabbit, the trap can be forgotten about.

5 Language is the same way.

6 After the meaning has been transmitted, the words can be dispensed with.

Language is the process, not the goal. What's the difference between going strictly by the book (even to the point of exhaustively studying the classics) and "concentrating on the branches in neglect of the roots"?

自然的箫声——庄子说Ⅰ

荃者所以在鱼，得鱼而忘荃；蹄者所以在兔，得兔而忘蹄；言者所以在意，得意而忘言。吾安得夫忘言之人而与之言哉！

《庄子◎外物第二十六》

99

自然的箫吉——主子说 I

《庄子◎寓言第二十七》

其往也，舍者迎将，其家公执席，妻执巾栉，舍者避席，炀者避灶，其反也，舍者与之争席矣。

老子曰：「而睢睢盱盱，而谁与居！大白若辱，盛德若不足。」阳子居蹴然变容曰：「敬闻命矣！」

敬，今闲矣，请问其过。」

阳子居不答。至舍，进盥漱巾栉，脱屦户外，膝行而前曰：「向者弟子欲请夫子，夫子行不闲，是以不敢，今闲矣，请问其过。」

阳子居南之沛，老聃西游于秦，邀子郊，至于梁而遇老子。老子中道仰天而叹曰：「始以汝为可教，今不可也。」

Zi Gong's Snow White Clothes

Yuan Xian and Zi Gong were students of Confucius.

1

Yuan Xian was very poor. He lived in a house where the roof leaked...

2

And there was a big hole in one of the walls. But he didn't mind.

3

Zi Gong was a wealthy government official, and one day he paid a visit to Yuan Xian.

4

The lane is too narrow, sir. The carriage won't fit.

5

原宪应之曰：「宪闻之，无财谓之贫，学而不能行谓之病。今宪，贫也，非病也。」

子贡曰：「嘻！先生何病？」

子贡乘大马，中绀而表素，轩车不容巷，往见原宪。原宪华冠纵履，杖藜而应门。

原宪居鲁，环堵之室，茨以生草，蓬户不完，桑以为枢；而瓮牖二室，褐以为塞；上漏下湿，匡坐而弦。

自然的箫声——庄子说Ⅰ

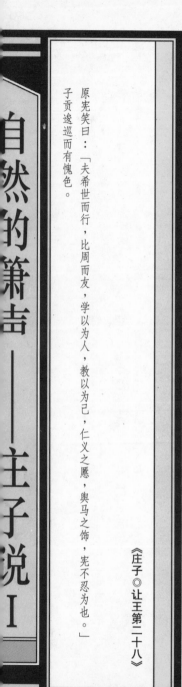

《庄子◎让王第二十八》

原宪笑曰：「夫希世而行，比周而友，学以为人，教以为己，仁义之慝，舆马之饰，宪不忍为也。」

子贡逡巡而有愧色。

自然的箫声——主子说Ⅰ

The Villain Speaks

Liu Xiaji was a friend of Confucius and had a little brother named Dao Zhi. Dao Zhi had nine thousand followers and together, they ravaged the land.

1

Parents should teach their children and older brothers should teach their younger brothers. Your little brother is a terrible villain and ravages the land. Isn't there anything you can do?

What can I do? Some people just don't listen.

2

3

Well, then let me have a try!

Look, my brother has a bad temper. If you cross him, I can't say what might happen. I think it would be better if you didn't go.

4

5

自然的箫声——庄子说 I

柳下季曰：「先生言为人父者必能诏其子，为人兄者必能教其弟，若子不听父之诏，弟不受兄之教，虽今丘请为先生往说之。」

丘请为先生往说之。」

弟，则无贵父子兄弟之亲矣。今先生，世之才士也，弟为盗跖，为天下害，而弗能教也，丘窃为先生羞之。

孔子谓柳下季曰：「夫为人父者，必能诏其子；为人兄者，必能教其弟。若父不能诏其子，兄不能教其

牛马，取人妇女，贪得忘亲，不顾父母兄弟，不祭先祖。所过之邑，大国守城，小国入保，万民苦之。

孔子与柳下季为友，柳下季之弟，名曰盗跖。盗跖从卒九千人，横行天下，侵暴诸侯，穴室枢户，驱人

103

前，见谒者曰：「鲁人孔丘，闻将军高义，敬再拜谒者。」

孔子不听，颜回为驭，子贡为右，往见盗跖。盗跖乃方休卒徒大山之阳，脍人肝而馆之。孔子下车而

先生之辩，将奈之何哉！且跖之为人也，心如涌泉，意如飘风，强足以距敌，辩足以饰非，顺其心则喜，逆

其心则怒，易辱人以言。先生必无往。

Confucius disregarded the warning, and with his disciples Zi Gong and Yan Hui, went to see Dao Zhi.

General, Confucius is outside. He wants to see you.

Rrrrrr!

Take a message to him. Tell him to stop confusing right and wrong and stop meddling in the affairs of the land's kings and princes.

Tell him to stop cheating people through his supposed morality. His sins are great. Tell him that if he hurries, he can get down the mountain before I get him!

Otherwise, I'll have his heart and liver for lunch!

Yes sir.

自然的箫吉——主子悦Ⅰ

盗跖大怒曰：「丘来前！夫可规以利而可谏以言者，皆愚陋恒民之谓耳。今长大美好，人见而悦之者，此吾父母之遗德也。丘虽不吾誉，吾独不自知邪？且吾闻之，好面誉人者，亦好背而毁之。今丘告我以大城众民，是欲规我以利而恒民畜我也，安可久长也！城之大者，莫大乎天下矣。尧舜有天下，子孙无置锥之地；汤武立为天子，而后世绝灭；非以其利大故邪？」

孔子再拜趋走，出门上车，执辔三失，目芒然无见，色若死灰，据轼低头，不能出气。归到鲁东门外，

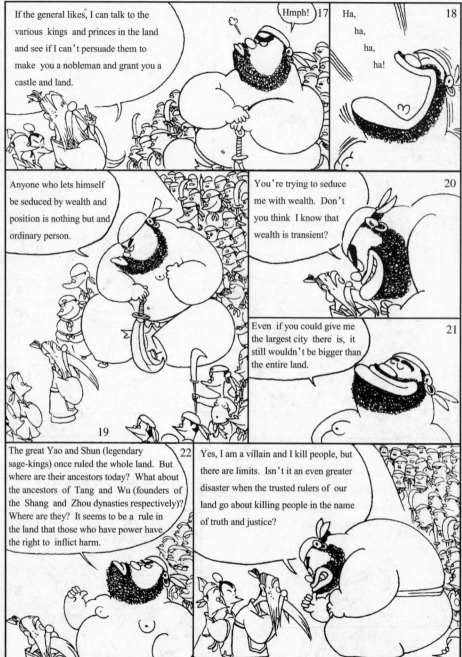

太子曰：「闻夫子明圣，谨奉千金以币从者。夫子弗受，悝尚何敢言！」

太子乃使人以千金奉庄子。庄子弗受，与使者俱，往见太子曰：「太子何以教周，赐周千金？」

太子悝患之，募左右曰：「孰能说王之意止剑士者，赐之千金。」左右曰：「庄子当能。」

昔赵文王喜剑，剑士夹门而客三千余人，日夜相击于前，死伤者岁百余人，好之不厌。如是三年，国衰，诸侯谋之。

必儒服而见王，事必大逆。」

太子曰：「然吾王所见剑士，皆蓬头突鬓垂冠，曼胡之缨，短后之衣，瞋目而语难，王乃说之。今夫子

庄子曰：「诺。周善为剑。」

太子曰：「然。吾王所见，唯剑士也。」

庄子曰：「闻太子所欲用周者，欲绝王之喜好也。使臣上说大王而逆王意，下不当太子，则身刑而死，

周尚安所事金乎？使臣上说大王，下当太子，赵国何求而不得也！」

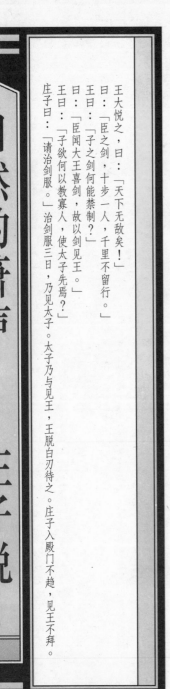

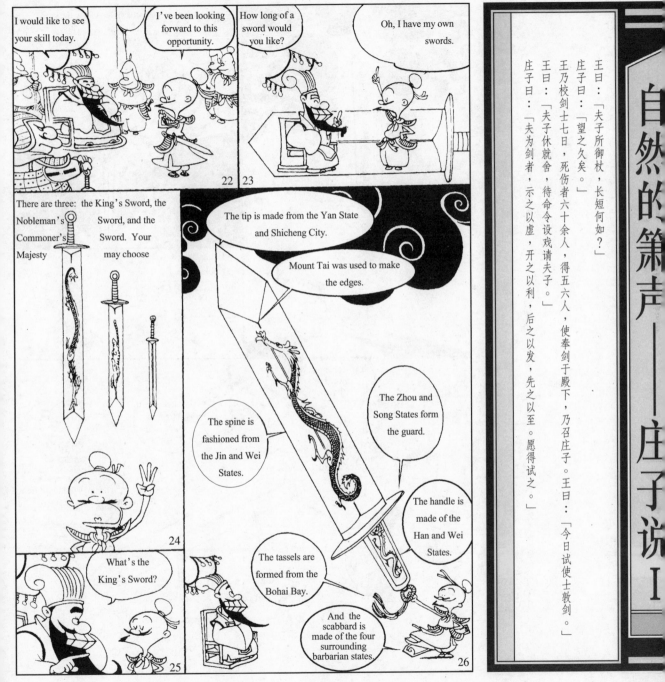

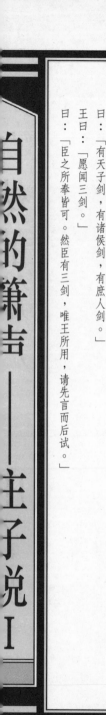

自然的箫吉——主子兑Ⅰ

曰：「臣之所奉皆可。然臣有三剑，唯王所用，请先言而后试。」

王曰：「愿闻三剑。」

曰：「有天子剑，有诸侯剑，有庶人剑。」

王曰：「天子之剑何如？」

曰：「天子之剑，以燕谿石城为锋，齐岱为锷，晋魏为脊，周宋为镡，韩魏为夹；包以四夷，裹以四

31

Released from its scabbard, East and West pay homage to it, North and South hold it in awe. That is the Nobleman's sword.

32

Then, what's the Commoner's Sword?

The Commoner's Sword has messy hair, a raspy voice, and eyes that belong on a dead fish.

33

Drawn from it's sheath, it seeks to chop off the enemy's head and cut out his heart; not much different from cock fighting. As soon as death is achieved, its mission is ended.

Unfortunately, Your Majesty prefers the Commoner's Sword.

34

!!!!

35

剑，直之亦无前，举之亦无上，案之亦无下，运之亦无旁，上法圆天以顺三光，下法方地以顺四时，中和民意以安四乡。此剑一用，匡诸侯，天下服矣。此天子之剑也。」

文王芒然自失，曰：「诸侯之剑何如？」

曰：「诸侯之剑，以知勇士为锋，以清廉士为锷，以贤良士为脊，以忠圣士为镡，以豪杰士为夹。此剑，直之无前，举之无上，案之无下，运之无旁，上决浮云，下绝地纪。此剑一用，如雷霆之震也，四封之内，无不宾服而听从君命者矣。此诸侯之剑也。」

「庶人之剑何如？」

曰：「庶人之剑，蓬头突鬓垂冠，曼胡之缨，短后之衣，瞋目而语难，相击于前，上斩颈领，下决肝肺，此庶人之剑，无异于斗鸡，一旦命已绝矣，无所用于国事。今大王有天子之位而好庶人之剑，臣窃为大王薄之。」

113

于是文王不出宫三月，剑士皆服毙其处也。

王乃牵而上殿。宰人上食，王三环之。庄子曰：「大王安坐定气，剑事已毕奏矣。」

王薄之。

肺。此庶人之剑，无异于斗鸡，一旦命已绝矣，无所用于国事。今大王有天子之位而好庶人之剑，臣窃为大

王曰：「庶人之剑，蓬头突鬓垂冠，曼胡之缨，短后之衣，瞋目而语难。相击于前，上斩颈领，下决肝

王曰：「庶人之剑何如？」

意以安四乡。此剑一用，如雷霆之震也，四封之内，无不宾服而听从君命者矣。此诸侯之剑也。」

《庄子◎说剑第三十》

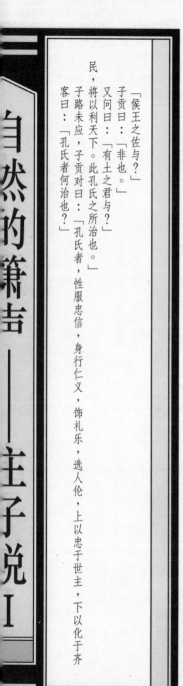

To do what you shouldn't is called: **Intemperance.**
To talk incessantly even though people don't listen is called: **Obsequiousness.**
To speak only what people wish to hear in order to gain their favor is called: **Flattery.**
To follow others without question is called: **Coquetry.**
To enjoy criticizing others is called: **Calumniation.**
To break up other people's relationships is called: **Craftiness.**
To praise the wicked and shun those you dislike is called: **Perfidy.**
To curry favor without regard for good or evil is called: **Duplicity.**

Extended outward, these eight shortcomings will wreak havoc on other people, and directed inward, they will do great harm to the self. They are things wise people do not approach.

To seek fame through great deeds is called: **Ostentation.**

To act with reckless disregard for others, selfishly carrying out your own plans is called: **Avarice.**

To see your own mistakes but not change; to hear other people's good advice but not act on it is called: **Malevolence.**

To call right those opinions in agreement with yours and call wrong those opinions not in agreement with yours even though they may be good is called: **Arrogance.**

And what are the four failings?

15

16

It's difficult to talk about the Dao with one who possesses these four failings.

17

If you want to attain great wisdom, don't be guilty of the eight shortcomings: intemperance, obsequiousness, flattery, coquetry, calumniation, craftiness, perfidy, and duplicity. And don't be caught with the four failings: ostentation, avarice, malevolence, and arrogance. These eight shortcomings and four failings are the mistakes most often committed.

Confucius' face turned pale and he bowed three times before departing.

18

自然的箫声——庄子说

《庄子◎渔父第三十一》

而始可教已。」

更，闻谏愈甚，谓之很；人同于己则可，不同于己，虽善不善，谓之矜。此四患也。能去八疵，无行四患，

君不臣。所谓四患者：好经大事，变更易常，以挂功名，谓之叨；专知擅事，侵人自用，谓之贪；见过不

人，谓之慝；不择善否，两容频适，偷拔其所欲，谓之险。此八疵者，外以乱人，内以伤身，君子不友，明

希意道言，谓之谄；不择是非而言，谓之谀；好言人之恶，谓之谗；析交离亲，谓之贼；称誉诈伪以败恶

客曰：「……且人有八疵，事有四患，不可不察也。非其事而事之，谓之总；莫之顾而进之，谓之佞；

孔子再拜而起曰：「丘少而修学，以至于今，六十九岁矣，无所得闻至教，敢不虚心！」

子贡曰：「非也。」……

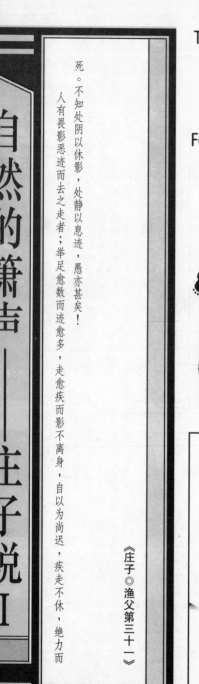

自然的箴言——庄子兑 I

死。不知处阴以休影，处静以息迹，愚亦甚矣！

人有畏影恶迹而去之走者；，举足愈数而迹愈多，走愈疾而影不离身，自以为尚迟，疾走不休，绝力而

《庄子◎渔父第三十一》

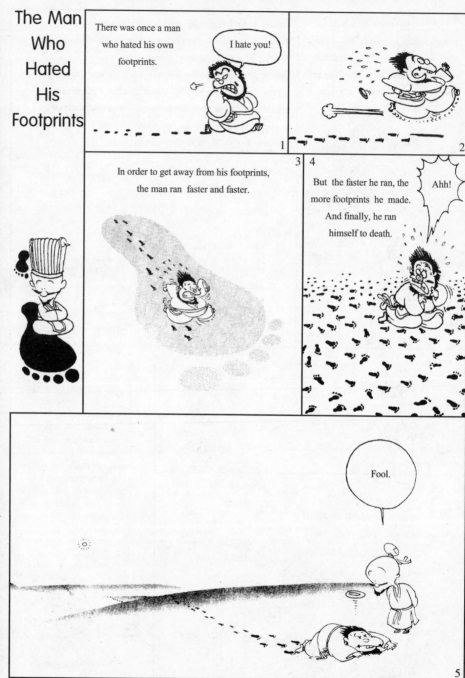

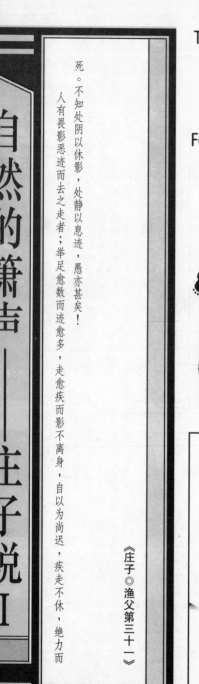

The Man Who Hated His Shadow

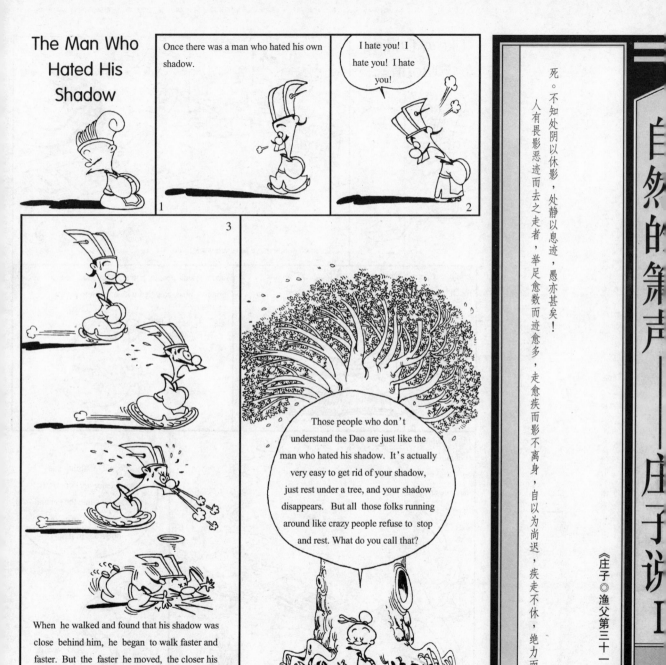

Once there was a man who hated his own shadow.

1

I hate you! I hate you! I hate you!

2

3

When he walked and found that his shadow was close behind him, he began to walk faster and faster. But the faster he moved, the closer his shadow came. So he ran like a madman... and in the end, he dropped dead.

Those people who don't understand the Dao are just like the man who hated his shadow. It's actually very easy to get rid of your shadow, just rest under a tree, and your shadow disappears. But all those folks running around like crazy people refuse to stop and rest. What do you call that?

人有畏影恶迹而去之走者，举足愈数而迹愈多，走愈疾而影不离身，自以为尚迟，疾走不休，绝力而死。不知处阴以休影，处静以息迹，愚亦甚矣！

《庄子◎渔父第三十一》

119

巧者劳而知者忧，无能者无所求，饱食而敖游，汎若不系之舟，虚而敖游者也。

《庄子○列御寇第三十二》

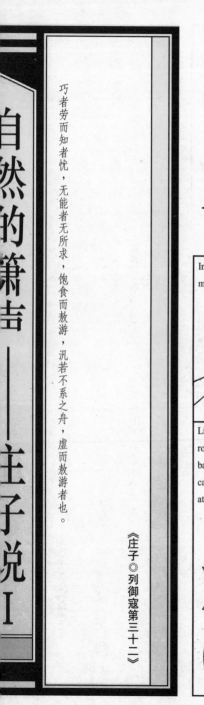

Like a Drifting Boat

1 Talented people have so much work to do.

2 Intelligent people have so much to worry about.

3 Incompetent people, however, go about in a dreamy bliss, satisfied with enough to eat.

4 Like an unmoored boat, drifting on the water, rocking gently back and forth, carefree and at ease.

People of ability and intelligence are constantly distressed, while the general population carries on oblivious to it all.

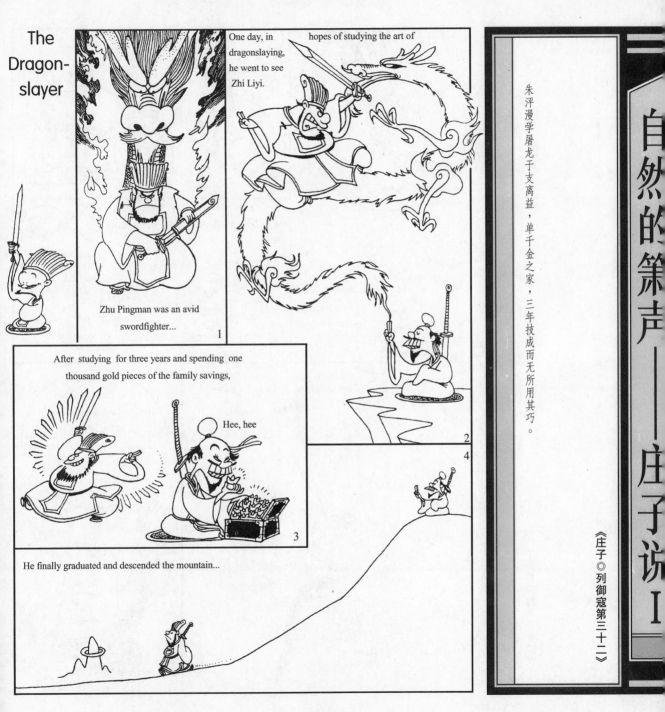

The Dragon-slayer

Zhu Pingman was an avid swordfighter...

1

One day, in hopes of studying the art of dragonslaying, he went to see Zhi Liyi.

2

After studying for three years and spending one thousand gold pieces of the family savings,

Hee, hee

3

He finally graduated and descended the mountain...

4

自然的箫声——庄子说 I

朱泙漫学屠龙于支离益，单千金之家，三年技成而无所用其巧。

《庄子○列御寇第三十二》

121

朱泙漫学屠龙于支离益，单千金之家，三年技成而无所用其巧。

《庄子◎列御寇第三十二》

Shattering the Dragonpearl

自然的箫声——庄子说 I

人有见宋王者，锡车十乘，以其十乘骄稚庄子。

庄子曰：「河上有家贫恃纬萧而食者，其子没于渊，得千金之珠。其父谓其子曰：『取石来锻之！夫千

金之珠，必在九重之渊而骊龙颔下，子能得珠者，必遭其睡也。使骊龙而寤，子尚奚微之有哉！』」

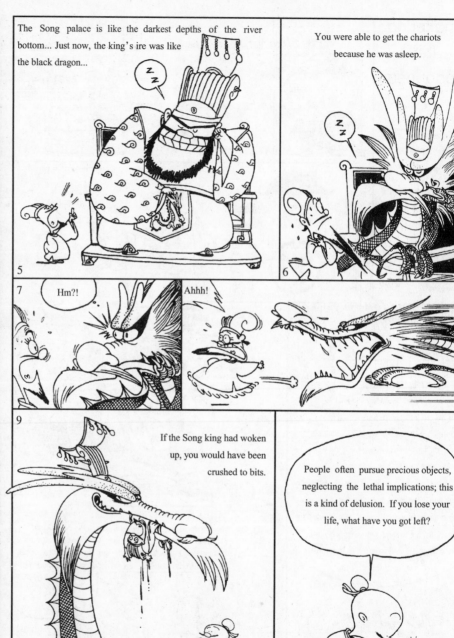

「今宋国之深，非直九重之渊也；宋王之猛，非直骊龙也；子能得车者，必遭其睡也。使宋王而寤，子

为齑粉夫！」

《庄子◎列御寇第三十二》

124

Don't Make Sacrifices

1. Our king would like you to be an official for the state.

   Sorry...

2. Do you see that sacrificial cow over there? Everyday it eats the best feed and is covered by a beautifully embroidered blanket,

3. But when the day comes for it to be brought into the temple and laid upon the sacrificial alter, it will be too late for its sudden wish to go back to the field and live like the rest of the cows.

或聘于庄子。庄子应其使曰：「子见夫牺牛乎？衣以文绣，食以刍叔，及其牵而入于大庙，虽欲为孤犊，其可得乎！」

《庄子◎列御寇第三十二》

125

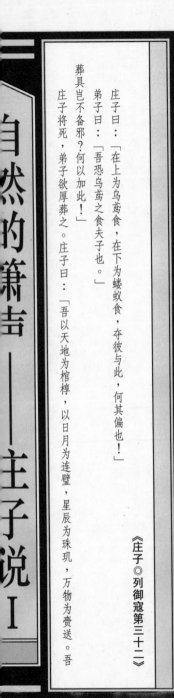

《庄子◎列御寇第三十二》

自然的萧声——主子说 I

庄子将死，弟子欲厚葬之。庄子曰：「吾以天地为棺椁，以日月为连璧，星辰为珠玑，万物为赍送。吾

葬具岂不备邪？何以加此！」

弟子曰：「吾恐乌鸢之食夫子也。」

庄子曰：「在上为乌鸢食，在下为蝼蚁食，夺彼与此，何其偏也！」

Zhuangzi on His Deathbed

126

图字：01-2005-0835

图书在版编目（CIP）数据

庄子说 I = Zhuangzi Speaks I：The Music of Nature/蔡志忠绘 . 一北京：现代出版社，2005
ISBN 7-80188-514-7

I . 庄… II . 蔡… III . 漫画-作品集-中国-现代 IV . J228.2

中国版本图书馆 CIP 数据核字（2005）第 025584 号

Zhuangzi Speaks I：The Music of Nature
庄子说 I：自然的箫声

作者/〔台湾〕蔡志忠
译者/〔美〕Brian Bruya
总策划/吴江江
责任编辑/张　璐
封面设计/刘　刚
出版发行/现代出版社（北京安外安华里 504 号　邮编：100011）
印刷/北京平谷早立印刷厂
开本/880×1230　1/24　5.5 印张
版次/2005 年 5 月第 1 版
　　　2005 年 5 月第 1 次印刷
印数/1～6000 册
书号/ISBN 7-80188-514-7
定价/13.50 元